ALONG THE SUNSHINE TRAIL

THE PROSE AND POETRY SERIES

FLOY WINKS DeLANCEY

WILLIAM J. IVERSON

ALONG THE SUNSHINE TRAIL

THE L. W. SINGER COMPANY

SYRACUSE   CHICAGO

The Authors

FLOY WINKS DeLANCEY

Associate Professor of English,
State University of New York, College of Education at Brockport

WILLIAM J. IVERSON

Professor of Education and Specialist in Reading,
Stanford University

Book Design by

STEFAN SALTER

Illustrations by

GUY BROWN WISER ASSOCIATES

Claude Leet, Richard Foes, Ken Smith

CONTENTS

UNIT ONE ANIMAL ADVENTURES

UNIT TWO YOUR FAMILY AND MINE

UNIT THREE   HAPPY STORIES OLD AND NEW

UNIT FOUR   CHILDREN'S THEATER

UNIT FIVE   OUR LAND LONG AGO

UNIT SIX   FARAWAY PLACES

UNIT SEVEN   A LONG STORY

UNIT ONE

ANIMAL
ADVENTURES

GORDON

THE GOAT

Munro Leaf

Gordon was a goat and he lived in Texas.

He liked to eat, and it didn't matter very much to him what he ate.

He would try anything.

Mostly he ate leaves from the mesquite trees.

But he would just as soon try a dishtowel off the line, or a ham from the smoke house if he could get in.

And every now and then he'd even bite a cactus, but he was sorry every time he did.

Gordon lived on a ranch with a lot of other goats. He didn't work very hard. All he did was just go on being Gordon day after day, and every once in a while he would get his hair cut.

The men who cut his hair called it mohair, and they sold it to other people. They used it to weave things like cloth and stuff things like cushions. That was all right with Gordon. He didn't care what they did with his hair just so they didn't nick him while they were cutting it off.

"Gordon the Goat" reprinted by permission of the author.

11

On the ranch where Gordon lived there were some goats that were called lead goats, because the other goats followed them around.

If a lead goat was at one place and he decided he didn't want to be there any longer, he would go somewhere else and all the other goats would tag along behind him. Sometimes where he went was better than where he had been and sometimes it was worse, but better or worse, when he went the rest of the goats all went along.

Gordon went, too. He never quite knew why. He didn't like any of the lead goats very much. But he didn't dislike any of them very much either.

So when all the others started off behind the leader, the easiest thing for Gordon to do was just to go along, too. That's what he did, and most of the time he waited so long before he decided to go that all the other goats were up ahead and he was at the tail end of the line.

One very hot day, the lead goat decided he

didn't like where he was, so he started out for some place different. He thought he remembered seeing some weeds he had never tried before over on the other side of a hill. Off he went to find the new weeds, and along went the rest of the goats, with Gordon at the end.

After a long, hot, hard walk they found the new weeds, but they weren't much good. Gordon ate some, but he wasn't quite sure that they made him feel very well.

After a while he began to be pretty sure that he was sorry he had come along at all.

So he sat down and decided to stay there until he felt better. But just when Gordon was getting comfortable, the lead goat decided to go somewhere else.

So away he went with the other goats behind him, and the very last was Gordon, who really didn't feel like going at all.

While he walked along with the hot sun beating

13

down on him, Gordon wondered and wondered just why he had come along. He was trying to figure out why he didn't do some thinking for himself instead of just following all the other goats who followed the lead goat just because that was what they always did.

It didn't seem to make sense to Gordon.

While he was deciding this quietly to himself, Gordon noticed that way off ahead of all the goats there was a big, dark, dusty looking thing coming right at them.

It started on the ground and stretched clear up into the sky and was bigger than anything Gordon had ever seen before. Gordon didn't like the looks of it one bit, and it kept right on coming at them faster and faster. Gordon wished that the lead goat would go somewhere else instead of straight ahead, but he didn't. So on they walked and at them it came until there they were — right in the middle of a twister. Now, a twister, or tornado, is no fun to be in, and Gordon was scared. Up he flew in a black wet cloud that tossed him round and round, upside down and downside up all at the same time.

Other things, caught in the twister too, bumped against him till he was sore and bruised and could hardly catch his breath.

With all the going round and round, Gordon
grew sorrier and sorrier that he had ever eaten
those new weeds.

First he turned yellow and then he turned green
and then he was sick. Gordon felt sorrier for
Gordon than he ever had before in his life. When
he had reached the point where he felt that he
couldn't last much longer, he saw the old lead
goat go whirling past him higher and higher and
he looked as though he felt even worse than

Gordon. Just then an extra sudden puff and swirl shot Gordon out through the edge of the twister, and he landed with a thud in the middle of a field that was soft enough to keep him from breaking his bones, but hard enough to hurt a lot.

After a long long while, Gordon got up slowly and looked around. He was stiff and bruised and he ached all over, but he knew something now that he wouldn't forget.

Never again would he just tag along from one place to another just because everyone else did. He was going to find out first where he was going, why he was going, and what he was going to do when he got there.

Gordon does his own thinking now, and he gets along much better than before.

16

WHAT HAPPENED?

Gordon was a goat with extra special hair. People made his hair into cloth and cushions. What was his hair called?

Gordon followed the lead goat just as the other goats did. Sometimes the goat led them to good things. Sometimes he didn't. One day he led Gordon and the other goats right into the middle of a dark, dusty storm stretching clear up to the sky. What do you call a storm like that?

That was enough for Gordon. He made up his mind to one thing for sure. What did Gordon decide?

THINK IT OVER

Usually it's easier just to follow somebody else. You don't have to think at all then. You don't worry about whether everybody agrees or not. But, if you belong to Scouts or some group like that, you try to share in deciding things. That means you do have to think and it is harder to get everybody to agree. What do you gain by letting everybody help to decide?

Letting everybody share doesn't mean you don't need a leader for a group. Someone has to help the group do whatever it decides to do. How does the leader help the group? How does the group help the leader?

17

THE JOLLY WOODCHUCK

Marion Edey

The woodchuck's very very fat,
But doesn't care a pin for that.

When nights are long and the snow is deep,
Down in his hole he lies asleep.

Under the earth is a warm little room
The drowsy woodchuck calls his home.

Rolls of fat and fur surround him,
With all his children curled around him,

Snout to snout and tail to tail.
He never awakes in the wildest gale;

When icicles snap and the north wind blows,
He snores in his sleep and rubs his nose.

MAGGIE, A MISCHIEVOUS MAGPIE

Irma Simonton Black

Some people have cats and some people have dogs. Some people have magpies! That is what Mr. and Mrs. Anderson had for a pet. And guess what they called her? Maggie, of course.

Maggie was a very pretty bird, much bigger than a robin. Her head and shoulders were shiny black and her breast was as white as snow. Maggie had a long beautiful tail — longer than all the rest of her. When the sun shone on her black feathers they gleamed, and looked green and blue and purple. . . .

Maggie stole so many things and got into so much mischief that Mr. and Mrs. Anderson began to worry.

She hid peanuts under the rugs and they went CRUNCH when people walked on them. She pecked at the ornaments on people's hats.

"Maggie, a Mischievous Magpie" from *Maggie, a Mischievous Magpie* by Irma Simonton Black. By permission of Holiday House, Inc.

"Perhaps Maggie needs a few toys of her own," said Mrs. Anderson. "Then she won't steal our things."

"Yes, perhaps," Mr. Anderson said.

He didn't really think anything would help, but he didn't want to say so. He liked Maggie very much.

So they bought some presents just for Maggie. They knew she liked shiny things, so they bought a few marbles. They knew she liked noisy things, so they bought a little bell. They knew she liked hats, so they bought her a tiny straw doll's hat for her very own.

They didn't give Maggie her presents right away. They thought they would wait until she looked as if she were going to get into mischief.

That afternoon some friends stopped in to see them. It was hot, so Mrs. Anderson fixed a pitcher full of lemonade, and cookies.

She warned the guests to hold on tight to their glasses.

They all sat in the yard chairs. Mr. and Mrs. Anderson kept an eye on Maggie. Maggie seemed to know it, too.

20

She flew to the ground and strutted in front
of everyone, as if she were saying,

"I'm very smart (Please look at me).
I'm very pretty (As you can see)."

Then she flew back into the tree, and began
to chatter and hop from one branch to another.
She seemed to be planning some naughty trick.

Then she flew down and lit on the back of Mr. Anderson's chair and cocked an eye at his glass.

Mr. Anderson held on firmly to his lemonade and reached in his pocket for a marble. He set it on the table where it would shine in the sun. Then he waited.

Maggie waited, too. She strutted about the yard and said, "Come here, Maggie, come here, Maggie," when anyone tried to talk.

Next she flew to the back of an empty chair and pretended to scratch her head. Then she smoothed her glossy feathers.

When no one was looking at her, Maggie flew down to the table, snatched the bright marble, and flew away.

Maggie was gone for about five minutes. Then she came back without the marble. She walked past the guests — and suddenly stopped. She cocked her neat black head and eyed the foot she saw in front of her.

Bare toes were showing out of the guest's sandal. They moved.

PECK! went Maggie and OUCH! went the guest.

"Oh, dear," Mrs. Anderson said.

She tinkled the small bell and put it on the table. Maggie tipped her head and listened. When she didn't hear the little sound again, she flew up to the table and looked at the bell. It was shiny and pretty, but very quiet.

On the top of the bell there was a loop. Maggie took this in her beak and flew off.

Tinkle-tinkle! went the bell. Maggie flew high in the elm tree just overhead and sat there shaking her bell.

It was easy to see that she was having a lot of fun. But then she dropped the bell. It fell a few feet and caught firmly on a small leafy twig.

Just about that time, the guests began to talk to each other. Maggie saw that they were paying no attention to her. She didn't like that. She flew to the bell, and shook it until the bell went "tinkle-tinkle-*tinkle-tinkle!*"

The bell made such a little sound that no one paid attention to it. Maggie flew down once more, talking and squawking.

(This time the guest with the bare toes covered her feet with her handkerchief.)

"Come here, Maggie, come here, Maggie," Mrs. Anderson said.

"Comeremaggie, comeremaggie," Maggie repeated, and flew to her mistress' chair and held on with her strong black feet.

Right next to Mrs. Anderson sat a guest with a straw hat. On the hat there was a bunch of red

shiny cherries. Mrs. Anderson saw
Maggie look at the hat, first with one
bright eye, then with the other. She
knew Maggie loved anything red and
shiny.

Mr. Anderson reached in his pocket
and brought out the toy hat.

Just for fun he put it on his own
head, and everybody laughed. He did
look funny.

Maggie flew to him at once, and
perched on his chair, looking at the hat.

Then, just as Mr. Anderson had
expected, she quickly snatched the hat
in her beak. She flew off before anyone
could stop her.

Maggie loved the hat more than the
other toys. Perhaps she loved it more
because they tried to get her to bring
it back.

They didn't want to take the hat
away. They wanted to try it on her
glossy head.

But Maggie was sure they wanted to
take it away. All afternoon she hopped
around in the tree, holding the hat in
her bill.

That kept her busy and out of mischief, and that was fine.

After the guests left, Mr. and Mrs. Anderson talked about Maggie.

"We can't get a bagful of toys every time we have guests," Mr. Anderson said. "She's *very* naughty."

"Maybe she's lonesome," Mrs. Anderson said. "Maybe she needs another bird or an animal of some kind."

They decided to get Maggie a playmate. They thought that would fix everything.

The playmate that Mr. and Mrs. Anderson chose for Maggie was a puppy. Since this puppy was to play with a bird, they chose a small one. He was so small that they named him Midge (for Midget).

Midge was no bigger than Maggie. He was black and white like Maggie, so that they looked very pretty together. But Maggie was smooth and shining, and the puppy was shaggy and rough.

25

When the Andersons brought Midge home in a little basket, they set him down in the yard. Maggie flew over at once. She was curious about new things.

This present was better than the bell, or the marbles, or the hat. This present moved all by itself.

Maggie perched on the edge of the basket. She looked him all over with one black mischievous eye. Then she turned her head and looked him all over with the other eye.

Maggie knew she couldn't pick up *this* toy and hide it in a tree! It was too big.

Maggie didn't know what to do. She hopped off the edge of the basket and walked around it. She chattered to herself.

Mrs. Anderson took Midge out of the basket and put him on the ground. Maggie, of course, walked right up to Midge.

Midge was a friendly little dog, so he wagged

his shaggy tail. He took a wobbly step toward Maggie. He had never had a bird friend, but he liked the idea.

When Maggie saw Midge's tail waving back and forth she thought it was something to play with. SWISH — she flew over his head to get a better look at this new toy.

The puppy, of course, thought this was a new game. He leaned down on his front paws. That was the way he asked people — or birds — to play with him. He wagged his tail harder than ever.

This time Maggie swished over his head again, and she grabbed the end of his little tail in her long black beak.

That made Midge twist around so fast that all four paws slipped out from under him. He fell down on his side.

It didn't hurt Midge when Maggie grabbed his tail, because she got only a few of his shaggy hairs in her bill. It didn't hurt him when he fell

down either, because he was used to falling down.

It did surprise him, though, to have a bird chasing his tail. He started to run.

Maggie thought this was great fun. She ran right after him. The funny thing was that Maggie seemed to know that if she flew it would spoil the fun. Then she could catch Midge's tail too quickly and easily. She could run on her two strong black legs just as fast as Midge could on his four legs.

Mr. and Mrs. Anderson laughed while Maggie chased the puppy round and round.

Midge ran until his little pink tongue hung out, and he looked hot and tired. Mrs. Anderson filled a pan with cool fresh water and called him to come and drink.

Midge took a long noisy drink. He dribbled water all the way down his front.

Maggie watched him while he lap-lapped at the water. Then she hopped over and took a neat, careful bird drink.

She put her beak in the water and then tipped her head back so that the water ran down the inside of her throat. She did not spill a drop on her shining white front.

Maggie looked as if she were saying, "That's the way to drink, clumsy puppy!"

Mrs. Anderson picked up Midge and went in the house. Mr. Anderson picked up the basket and went in, too.

They didn't notice Maggie. She always stayed out until night.

But Maggie didn't want to miss a thing. She flew after them, and arrived just as the screen door banged shut. Maggie walked back and forth in front of the door, talking to herself in an angry way. Then she flew to the window sill and looked in.

Mrs. Anderson saw her and opened the door. By this time Midge was fast asleep in his basket. He lay all curled up with one floppy ear folded back over his head.

Maggie looked in the basket at Midge. Then she walked over to her cage, went in, and took a nap for herself!

"She likes him," Mrs. Anderson said. "He's going to be the very thing to keep her out of mischief."

WHAT HAPPENED?

Maybe Maggie thought that it was another marble. It was white, and round at the end. Anyway, Maggie took a good peck and the guest said, "Ouch!" What had Maggie pecked?

Maggie also had her eye on the bright red cherries on another guest's hat. But Mr. Anderson thought of something to draw her away from the cherries. He put it on his head and Maggie snatched it quickly. What did Mr. Anderson put on his head?

When Midge came to join Maggie as a pet at the Andersons', Maggie chased him all over. Midge had something that looked like a toy to Maggie. What was it?

Finally Maggie decided she liked Midge. How do you know Maggie felt that way?

THINK IT OVER

One way to write a good story is to fill it with interesting characters. Writers make characters interesting not only by letting you know just how they look, but also by telling you what they say and do. Maggie doesn't say very much. But she is doing something all the time. What do you learn about Maggie from watching what she does? For example, Maggie is attracted by every new thing. What does that tell you about her? What else does Maggie do which tells you something about her?

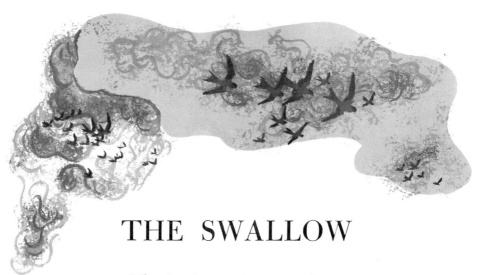

THE SWALLOW

Christina Rossetti

Fly away, fly away over the sea,
  Sun-loving swallow, for summer is done;
Come again, come again, come back to me,
  Bringing the summer and bringing the sun.

THE BEAR IS A HERO

Harrison Kinney

Stephen Thompson and his father grew very fond of a runaway circus bear named Henry. Stephen kept him in the old icehouse at night and tied him to a tree in the daytime. Mr. Thompson tried to get a license for the bear from Judge Holt, but the Judge said "No!" The people in Easton, including Stephen's mother, did not like having Henry around. Even though he was a tame bear, they were afraid of him. They thought the Thompsons should send Henry back to the circus.

One day Stephen's father didn't tie the knot in the bear's rope tight enough, and the bear got loose from the tree. Stephen discovered that the

"The Bear Is a Hero" reprinted by permission from *Lonesome Bear* by Harrison Kinney, published by McGraw-Hill Book Co., Inc. Copyright, 1949, by Harrison Kinney and Harold Price.

bear was missing when he got home from school that afternoon.

"The bear isn't here," shouted Stephen, running into the house.

"Oh, dear me!" said his mother. "You'd better run right down the street and tell your father."

So Stephen ran down the street toward his father's store. He was about to cross Elm Street when he heard a fire truck racing toward him. He waited for it to pass.

As the end of the long truck swung past him, Stephen suddenly saw the bear sitting on the rear platform of the fire truck. The firemen didn't seem to know the bear was riding with them, because the long ladder extended out over the bear's head.

Stephen ran the rest of the way to his father's store.

"The bear got loose!" Stephen told his father breathlessly. "I just saw him on the back end of the fire engine."

"Oh, dear heavens!" said his father, looking alarmed. "I hope nothing happens."

Stephen's father hurriedly put on his hat and coat.

"We'd better go right down to the fire station," he said to Stephen.

"Yes, sir," Stephen said.

The man and the little boy walked quickly toward the fire station, quite a distance away. By the time they arrived, the hook-and-ladder truck was back inside the building. The truck was always backed into the station house and parked, so Mr. Thompson and Stephen were unable to see the back of the truck or whether the bear was still there or not.

Sheriff Jones and Mr. Black, the Easton Fire Chief, were waiting for them.

"I've warned you about that bear making himself a public nuisance," Sheriff Jones shouted at Stephen's father.

"That was a practice run we just went out on," Mr. Black told Stephen's father angrily. "The County Fire Inspector wanted to know how quickly we could get to a certain street corner on the other side of town and get the hose hooked up. The Inspector was there timing us with a watch."

"Well, it didn't take you long," said Stephen's father, trying to sound pleasant.

"Of course it didn't!" howled the Fire Chief. "We couldn't get near the hose to unstring it. That dumb bear of yours was sitting on the back of the truck right in front of the hose locker. Nobody dared to go near him. The Easton Fire Department is now the laughing-stock of Aroostook County!"

"Robert, I've got to tell you again," Sheriff Jones said to Stephen's father. "Either you get rid of that bear or I'm going to have him shot as a public nuisance."

"I know," said Stephen's father quietly. "We're going to take the bear back to the woods next Saturday and lose him."

"He likes to ride on trucks and in cars," Stephen explained to the Sheriff and the Fire Chief.

"Well, let him ride in your father's car, then," said Mr. Black, the Fire Chief. "I don't want to find him on the back of my fire truck when I get to a fire. He's still back there, too. You'd better get him out of here."

35

So Stephen went around to the back of the
truck where the bear was sitting, waiting for the
truck to take him for another ride.

"We've got to take you home," Stephen told the
bear.

The bear followed Stephen out of the fire
station.   Then Stephen, his father, and the bear
walked sadly home. . . .

Mrs. Thompson was very much upset when she
learned that the bear had come back with her
husband and son.   She locked herself in her room
and refused to come out for several hours.

"I don't know why our home has to be turned
into a zoo," she told her husband tearfully.

"The circus will be back up this way in a few
weeks," Stephen's father said consolingly.   "We'll
give the bear back to them again."

That night Stephen and the bear waited on the
back steps for the boy's father to come out and
sing to them.   But he never did.   Mr. Thompson
was troubled because his wife and the Sheriff and
the people in the town did not like the bear.

One morning, two days later, Stephen discovered that the bear had got out of the icehouse

again. He searched in back of the apple orchard and he looked upstairs in the guest room, just for luck. Finally he started downtown to tell his father that the bear was loose again somewhere in Easton.

When Stephen was a block from the Farmers' Bank Building, he suddenly saw the brown bear trudge out of an alley and climb into the front seat of a long black automobile that was parked in front of the bank.

The engine was idling, and the front door had been left open. From the front seat the bear pushed himself over into the back and sat down on the floor of the car.

Stephen was looking at the bear through the car window when a bell in the bank began ringing loudly. Two men carrying guns and cloth sacks came running out of the bank and leaped into the front seat of the car.

"The bear's in there!" shouted Stephen, pointing at the bear through the car window.

But the men didn't hear him over the noise of the bell. They slammed the front door shut, and the car roared away.

A minute later, Stephen saw Sheriff Jones in his car, followed by two more cars filled with deputies, race down Main Street in the direction the big black car had taken.

Stephen ran the rest of the way to his father's store. His father was sitting behind his roller-top desk.

"The bear got in a car and the people drove away and didn't see him," Stephen said, panting for breath.

His father buried his face in his hands.

"Son," said his father, "this is the end. Those poor innocent people will find a bear in their car. They won't know that he's a tame bear. They'll get excited and drive right off the road and maybe kill themselves. If the bear gets out alive, he'll be shot. They may even put me in jail because I'm responsible for the animal's actions."

"Sheriff Jones is chasing the bear," Stephen said to his father.

"You and George will have to go with your mother to live with her family, now," said his father absently. "You must always be good to your mother, Son."

"Yes, sir," Stephen said.

Mr. Thompson calmly locked his desk. He and Stephen drove slowly home in the Dodge.

"Just don't talk to me for a while, Son," his father told Stephen. "I want to think about all this."

"Yes, sir," answered Stephen.

As they neared their house, Stephen saw a group of people standing on the front lawn. The Sheriff's car was parked in front of it.

"The bear is sitting in Sheriff Jones's car," said Stephen.

His father stopped the Dodge, and they got out. The Sheriff came toward them with a friendly smile on his face.

"Those bank robbers didn't even get out of town," the Sheriff told Stephen's father happily. "The driver spotted that bear of yours in the rearview mirror, sitting on the back seat. They went over the edge of the culvert at the bottom

of Mill Hill. I took them both without firing a shot. They're in the prison hospital, now."

Stephen's father looked bewildered. He sat down on the front steps of his house to think.

"The bear likes to ride in cars," Stephen said to the Sheriff.

"It's a good thing for all the people in this town with money in that bank that he does," the Sheriff answered. "He didn't get hurt a bit, either. We're going to give him part of the reward we will get for capturing those bank robbers."

Several children gathered around the Sheriff's car to look at the bear that had helped capture the bank robbers. The bear yawned and went to sleep on the back seat.

"We took him fishing so he'd go away in the woods," Stephen told the Sheriff. "But he got back in the car without our knowing it."

Sheriff Jones sat down on the steps beside Stephen's father.

"I saw Judge Holt at the prison hospital," the Sheriff said to Stephen's father. "The Judge was pretty pleased about the bear helping to capture those bandits. He doesn't see why the town can't give this bear a special license so he'll be protected."

"Why, by George!" said Stephen's father. "That's certainly good of the Judge. He's a good bear. We won't let him loose again."

Stephen went over to the bear and shook him awake. "You're a hero, I guess."

The bear followed him around the house, and Stephen locked the animal in the icehouse, after patting him on the head with pride.

Dinner was a very happy occasion that evening.

"Henry is certainly a famous bear now," said Stephen's mother pleasantly. "Everyone is talking about the way he saved the money."

"He saved the money we had in the bank," said her husband, "and the Sheriff says his share of the reward will be two hundred dollars."

"You can do a lot with two hundred dollars," Mrs. Thompson said. "I think it would be a nice thing if we fixed up the icehouse for the bear."

"We could have a nice yard fenced off for him to play in, too. Then he wouldn't have to be tied," Stephen's father added.

"We can buy him a lot of marshmallows now," Stephen said.

"We might screen in the back porch, too,"

Stephen's mother added. "I've always wanted that done."

"I think that might be arranged," said Mr. Thompson, winking at Stephen.

After dinner was finished that evening, Stephen and the bear sat down on the steps of the back porch. After a while Stephen's father came out, carrying his ukulele that was shaped like a banjo. He patted the bear on the head.

"Son, tomorrow we'll get the bear a new collar with a shiny metal license tag," Stephen's father said to him.

"Do you think we'll be able to fix the icehouse in time for him to sleep in it this winter?" Stephen asked.

"I'm pretty sure we can," his father replied. "You know, Easton is pretty proud of this bear. We must take good care of him."

"Yes, sir," said Stephen, patting the bear on the head.

Then Stephen's father began singing, "Oh, Dear,

Are You Lonesome Tonight?" while Stephen and the bear sat and listened to him. Stephen's father had a pleasant voice to listen to, and Stephen always knew that his father was happy when he sang.

WHAT HAPPENED?

The bear liked to ride in cars and trucks. The first time the bear got loose he found a fine truck to ride in. What was it?

The second ride the bear took was even more interesting. It was faster, too. With whom did the bear ride?

Everybody was grateful to the bear. Why was everybody grateful? The Judge was grateful. What did he do for the bear? The Sheriff was grateful, too. What did he do?

THINK IT OVER

If you saw a fourth grader riding in a baby carriage that would be funny, wouldn't it? We usually think something unexpectedly out-of-place is funny. A picture of a baby riding a bicycle would be just as funny as a fourth grader riding in a baby carriage.

This story has some things to make you laugh. Who does most of the unexpected, out-of-place things? What things does he do which you think are funny?

43

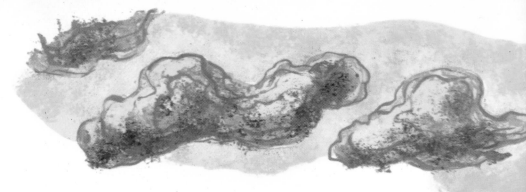

HORSE SONG

Hilda Faunce Wetherill

My horse is beautiful.
His tail is like a black cloud;
His mane is like a black cloud that floats in the
    sky;
His hooves are like black agate, hard and striped;
His legs are fast like the wind.
Like the holy winds,
He carries me over the long trails.

"Horse Song" from *Navajo Indian Poems* by Hilda Faunce Wetherill. By permission of Vantage Press, Inc.

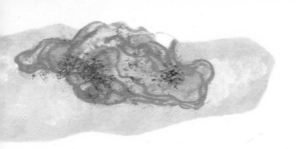

THE ADVENTURE IN THE CAVE

Grace and Carl Moon

Dat-say and Nah-wee are Indian children who live near the desert.

One morning Dat-say said to Nah-wee: "I have a trap down on the edge of the desert. I am going to see if there is anything in it. I may catch a coyote."

"I will go too," said Nah-wee, and she danced on the tips of her toes because she was so happy to go. All this morning she had wanted very much to go down into the desert, but her mother would not let her go alone. When she had first

opened her eyes and looked out at the golden sunshine and the blue sky and the white puffy clouds that were racing before the wind, she had thought how nice it would be to run down in the desert and find little stones of bright colors and watch the rabbits pop into the sage and eat piñon nuts and little berries that Dat-say knew how to find. Every day the desert seemed to be a different place to Nah-wee, and always there were so many things to do. And if Dat-say had made a trap it was very exciting to think what might be the thing that was in it. As they ran down the trail Nah-wee could see little puffs of dust in the desert, and far away, behind the blue hills, were great white clouds piled high in the sky.

46

"I like to see the clouds like that," she said to Dat-say. "I think maybe they are very big birds. I would like to feel how their feathers are soft."

"I think they are not birds," said Dat-say. "They are big white blankets, and they are full of water. My father says it will rain."

"It does not matter," laughed Nah-wee. "Water is nice, and my mother says it is the rain that makes the corn and the melons to grow."

"Water is nice when it is not falling down on you out of the sky," laughed Dat-say. "But look now, how the clouds are not white any more."

"BOOM–M!" went a big sound then, and Nah-wee and Dat-say both gave a jump. They were out in the desert now, very near to the place where the trap of Dat-say was laid.

47

"It is the Thunder Drum of the rain," said Dat-say. "Now will come the dance of the water. I think maybe it would be the best thing to go back up that trail."

"First we must see what is in the trap," begged Nah-wee. "Never have I seen a wild animal that is alive — maybe one is there." But when they got to the trap nothing was there at all. Dat-say could see very plainly that a something had been there, but now it was gone, and a little he was glad that it was so. Never had he caught a live thing, and he did not very much like the thought of it.

BOOM! BOOM! went that thunder sound again, and little drops of rain began to come down.

"Now we will get very wet," said Dat-say. "There is no place on that trail where the rain cannot come."

"But look!" said Nah-wee, and she pointed to a place on the side of the hill where a big flat rock stuck out in such a way that there was a shelter-place under it like a little room; "I think maybe we could get under that rock." And they both ran to the place, and they got under the rock before the very hardest rain came. There was just room enough for them both, and they were very glad to be there, for never had the rain come down harder than this time. It was like a river coming straight out of the sky, and they could not see anything outside of their little shelter-place at all. Then Dat-say gave a little cry.

"Look!" he said. "There is a hole back of this rock. I think it is a cave-place. I will see if I can go in." And sure enough there was a black hole that went into the side of the hill, and he put his head inside and began to crawl in, and Nah-wee watched him eagerly. Maybe there would be room inside for her to come too, and a cave was a very nice thing to find. But when

49

Dat-say was half inside he backed out again so quickly that he went right out into the rain, and he gave a little howl of surprise.

"There is a thing in that place!" he cried, "a live thing! I felt how it moved. It went against my face!"

"What is it?" cried Nah-wee, and she did not mind that the rain came down hard on them both.

"Maybe it is a bear!" said Dat-say, but then he knew very quickly that it could not be a bear. A bear could not go into a place that was so small, and almost any animal that he knew would have bitten him or would have growled when he came so close. He felt very curious about this one, and then suddenly he got down on his hands and knees again by the hole. "I think," he said, "I will go in and see what it is."

"Oh, no!" cried Nah-wee. "Do not go in that place again. Come out, Dat-say," and she caught hold of his arm and tried to pull him back. "Maybe it will eat you up." But already Dat-say was in that hole, and he felt very brave to have Nah-wee talk like that, but he did not have any fear of this thing in the cave — it could not be a very big thing. This time he reached in with his hands, and he brought out that live thing, and Nah-wee cried out when she saw it. It was very small and very soft and very brown. It was a BABY COYOTE!

"Oh!" said Nah-wee. "Oh, Dat-say! Let me

put my hands on it!" and it trembled when she touched it and tried to get away.

"I think the mother has been caught in some trap," said Dat-say. "Not ever will I make a trap again. And this one will maybe starve if we do not feed it. We must go fast up that trail. My mother will know the thing to do." And they forgot that the rain still came down very hard, and they forgot that the trail was steep, and remembered only to keep that little coyote very warm and dry in the dress of Nah-wee.

And Nah-wee all the time made little soft sounds with her mouth to feel that warm little thing so close.

Many people in the town came to see that little coyote and said it was a good thing that Dat-say had found it, for it was very hungry, and the mother must have been gone a long time. It could not have lived without the food they gave to it. But it did live, and grew to be tame like a little dog, so that it followed Nah-wee and Dat-say wherever they went, and not *ever* after that did Dat-say put any trap in the desert. He thought if he did that maybe he would catch some other mother coyote, and maybe somewhere a baby coyote would wait for food and no one would come.

"Traps are not good," said Dat-say, and Nah-wee nodded her head solemnly.

"For me," she said, "I like much better a little cave-place," and she looked very wise when she said it.

WHAT HAPPENED?

Dat-say and Nah-wee were glad to find the cave. But that wild animal really frightened them. Dat-say knew at once it wasn't a bear. How could he tell so quickly?

Dat-say decided not to trap animals any more. The animal in the cave helped him to decide. How did it help him?

THINK IT OVER

Dat-say and Nah-wee lived differently from most of you. They lived in an Indian village. They wore different clothes. They ate different food.

But in other ways Dat-say and Nah-wee were very much like you. They felt as you would when Dat-say bumped into the animal in the dark cave. How did they feel? When they saw the animal they acted just about the way you would. How did they act?

53

BENJAMIN AND WHISKERS

Marguerite Henry

Quite by accident Benjamin Watkins discovered that he owned a trick pup. One autumn morning as he rounded the corner of the house, Whiskers sat looking out at him from the open kitchen window.

Now the sill was a good six feet from the ground, and Whiskers had no thought at all of jumping. She was simply enjoying the warm September sunshine and the good smell of the air after last night's rain.

Without really thinking about tricks Benjamin looked up at Whiskers, crooked his arms, and cried, "Allay-oop!" in his best circus manner.

To his delight the little dog stood up on the window sill as if she thought something special was expected of her. Then she whimpered as she

"Benjamin and Whiskers" from *A Boy and His Dog* by Marguerite Henry. By permission of Wilcox and Follett.

always did when trying to understand a strange new command.

"ALLAY–OOP!" repeated Benjamin, with all the encouragement he could put into the silly words. And he lifted his arms a little higher.

This time Whiskers understood what he wanted. With a joyful bark she leaped and landed right in her master's arms.

"Gee whillakers!" whistled Benjamin. "Think of owning a trick pup and never knowing it!" He scratched Whiskers behind her upstanding black ear, and then behind her floppy white ear. He smoothed her whiskery face. "Think of it," he repeated softly, "Whiskers a trick pup! *Me* with a trick pup!"

"Benjamin Watkins!" came a shrill voice from inside the house. "You get going to school. It's five minutes of nine!"

"Sure, Ella. Thanks for telling me."

Gosh, thought Benjamin, wouldn't Pop be proud of how polite I was? It isn't so easy to be polite to Ella, even if she *is* trying to take Mom's place the best she knows how. . . .

All these things flickered through Benjamin's mind as quickly as lightning bugs. Then with a new tenderness he carried Whiskers to the dog-house. "Better sleep all day, Whiskers," he advised. "You and I are going into training."

The puppy peered around the door of her house and followed Benjamin with her eyes until he was completely out of sight. She knew better than to steal after him. Ella had taught her what happens to dogs that leave the yard.

Every Saturday, and every night after school, Benjamin and Whiskers worked on higher and higher jumps. Never was a pup more eager to learn! From the kitchen window Whiskers graduated to the roof of the tool shed. Then she managed to take the jump from the fork of the apple tree. The highest step was the crotch of a big oak tree.

By this time she was landing in Benjamin's arms with such force that he was afraid she might break a leg. So he rounded ·up four younger boys and taught them how to catch Whiskers in an old blanket he had wheedled from Ella.

As if it were part of the routine, Whiskers always whimpered before she jumped. And always she took courage when Benjamin repeated, "Allay-oop"

in a voice which clearly meant, "Come on, Whiskers. *I'm* here to catch you."

Before long the whole neighborhood knew that Whiskers was no ordinary pup. Even Benjamin's friend, Spud Milligan, admitted as much. (And Spud was something of an authority, for he owned a smart dog himself.) But how really remarkable Whiskers was, no one guessed — not until something unbelievable happened. For the first time in the history of Centerville, the Y.M.C.A. drive fell short of its quota. This was real calamity. Why, all winter long the "Y" was the center of things! Something certainly had to be done.

Benjamin called a meeting of the neighborhood boys at once. "I guess it's up to us fellows to raise the money," he explained. "After all, we're

the ones who use the 'Y.' What do you say we put on a circus?" And before the boys could answer, Benjamin went on talking as if he had rehearsed this speech many times.

"If I help Ella with the housecleaning, maybe she'll let us have the circus right here in the yard. We could build a platform high in the oak tree, and Whiskers could jump, and we could charge a nickel a jump."

The idea caught on like wildfire. Spud Milligan thought his bulldog, Jazbo, ought to be in the show, too. He could swing Jazbo round and round in a circle, while the dog held onto a rag with his teeth.

Dopey West thought his mother might make apples-on-a-stick to sell for a dime. Someone else knew where he could borrow an old phonograph and some band records.

The Saturday of the circus turned out to be one of those golden days in late October. The air was warm and gentle, although the trees were as bare as they are in midwinter. High up in the Watkins' oak tree, loops of gold fringe glittered and waved from a little square red platform. Leading to this platform was a long ladder. Benjamin still wished that he had trained Whiskers to climb the ladder by herself, but he had been so busy beating rugs and washing windows and even polishing silver for Ella that it was a wonder the circus had come into being at all.

But now the work was forgotten, and one could almost feel the bright expectancy that hung over the yard.

Dopey's mother *had* made the apples-on-a-stick, and they stood in rows on a long table covered with a red-and-white cloth. The tool shed had been transformed into a ticket office. It boasted a big handmade sign.

Already a few children were straggling in, looking up at the platform in the tree, and giggling.

In the basement of Benjamin's house, the boys were grooming Whiskers and Jazbo. No fancy show dogs were ever combed and brushed more lovingly. Whiskers' coat shone so that each hair looked as if it had been polished separately. And Jazbo was handsome and sleek in a bold sort of way.

"Hey, fellows," whispered Spud, "look at the crowd coming in! Even the milkman's taking time off to watch the show."

"Yep, and there's Mr. Svenson from the bakery."

"And there's the nice old lady who sells Mom her eggs."

"And there's stuck-up Gertie."

"Gosh, what a mob!"

Benjamin suddenly felt dizzy. Just supposing Whiskers had stage fright . . . Just supposing . . .

"Benjamin Watkins! For land's sakes, what you boys up to? These folks got other things to do besides wait for a couple of flea-bit mongrels to do tricks."

The audience heard Ella's remarks. They laughed and clapped their hands and shouted, "BRING 'EM ON!"

Spud and Jazbo were first. Spud was dressed in a high silk hat and a red shirt borrowed from his sister. He also wore fierce mustaches, but everyone knew him just the same.

From the ticket window of the tool shed came the sudden squeaking of a phonograph needle, then the blaring of a brass band. The ticket seller, who now had charge of sound effects, tried to soften the music, but he only succeeded in making it screech louder than ever.

Spud whipped a worn rag out of his sleeve.

"LADIES AND GENTLEMEN," he shouted above the trumpets and drums, "Jazbo-the-Bull is a superstitious animal. He refuses to swing on anything but his old yellow rag. When a dog is world-famous like Jazbo, he don't need red velvet or gold fringe." Here Spud winked toward the platform high up in the tree. "Bring on Jazbo-the-Bull," he called.

Quick as a flash the cellar door flew open and Jazbo-the-Bull streaked in the direction of Spud's voice. He grabbed the yellow rag, and Spud whirled him round and round while the music went faster, faster, faster.

Benjamin watched from the cellar window. "If only Whiskers does as well!" he prayed.

Then it was Whiskers' turn. Now Benjamin was climbing the ladder with Whiskers in one arm. Gently he set her down on the platform. For one instant he almost wished he were beating rugs for Ella, or even polishing silver.

Above the tittering of the children he could hear Mr. Svenson say to the milkman, "Ay bat you two bits the mutt never yumps."

63

Benjamin's four helpers stepped up. They wore firemen's helmets, and they clutched the four corners of the blanket as if their own lives, and Whiskers' too, depended on it.

Somehow Benjamin managed to scramble down the ladder. BOOM–BOOM! sounded the drums. Then, out of the stillness that followed, came Benjamin's trembling "Allay-oop" that somehow matched the shivering pup in the tree.

Benjamin had always thought of Whiskers as a medium-sized dog. Now she seemed the littlest of creatures, alone against the gnarled black branches and vast blue sky. She peered over the edge of the platform and whimpered.

"ALLAY–OOP!" repeated Benjamin. This time his voice rang out in the stillness. It said many things to Whiskers. She cocked her one black ear. She wagged her tail ever so slightly. Then

with a bark of joy she leaped nimbly into the air and landed in the blanket with a soft thud.

WHAT HAPPENED?

Whiskers was no ordinary dog. Benjamin taught her to jump from higher and higher places. What was the highest place from which she jumped?

That was the beginning of the neighborhood circus. Spud helped and Dopey helped. What were the boys going to do with the money they raised?

Jazbo-the-Bull was a great hit on the day of the circus. Benjamin wondered if Whiskers could do as well. Mr. Svenson was sure she wouldn't. What did Whiskers do to settle the matter?

THINK IT OVER

Many people are interested in helping boys and girls like you. Your parents and teachers are, of course. Then there are the people in groups like the 4–H Club and the Junior Red Cross. They like to do things for you.

But all these people sometimes need your help. You know ways to help your parents and teachers. Do you know ways to help people in other groups? It isn't always money they need. What other kinds of help do they need from you?

65

THOUGHTS IN BED

Marion Edey

Through animal paths in Africa
  The elephant walks alone.
The parrot calls in the forest wall
  Of a world that is all his own.

Far above his leafy roof
  A pink flamingo flies.
Great lizards cool their tails in the pool,
  Too lazy to open their eyes.

And when I lie in bed and hear
  The winter winds that come,
When the winter rain on the windowpane
  Is rolling like a drum,

I think of wildest Africa,
  Of jungles yet unknown,
Where the parrots squawk in parrot talk
  And the elephant walks alone.

UNIT TWO

YOUR FAMILY
AND MINE

MONEY

FOR HONEY

Marion Holland

It was a hot, sticky day right in the middle of summer vacation. Billy went over to Fats' house to see what Fats was doing. But Fats wasn't doing anything, either. He was sitting on his own front steps, with his head in his hands, and a big scowl on his face.

"Say, lend me two dollars," he said before Billy even got through the gate.

"What for?" asked Billy, not that he had two dollars. But as Fats knew perfectly well that he didn't and he knew that Fats knew it, there wasn't any sense mentioning it.

"To buy a book with," replied Fats.

"What you want to buy a book for?"

"I don't," said Fats gloomily, "but I have to."

Then he told Billy the whole thing. It seems he was reading a library book, and just as he got to the most interesting part, his mother suddenly got the idea that he ought to take a bath. Naturally he stalled as long as he could, figuring he would come to a good stopping place. But the longer he read, the more exciting the story got, and the more unreasonable his mother got. Finally he propped the book up on the edge of the bathtub

"Money for Honey" reprinted from *Billy Had a System* by Marion Holland, by permission of Alfred A. Knopf, Inc. Copyright, 1949, 1950, 1951, 1952, by Marion Holland.

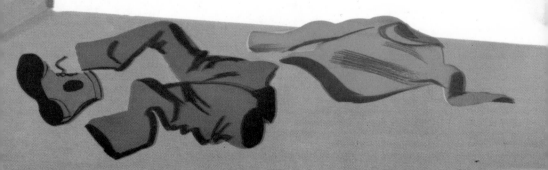

and went right on reading, making splashing noises with his feet every so often, so it would sound like somebody washing. It was a very handy arrangement — till the book fell into the tub.

"Naturally, I wiped it right off on the bath mat," said Fats indignantly. "But the lady at the library was very sniffy about it. She said the book was ruined, even though you can still read every single word in it. What's it matter if the pages did turn pink where the red ink came off the covers? So now she says I have to pay for the book, or I can't take any more books out of the library."

"What do you care?" asked Billy. "Any special book you want, I'll get it out for you on my card."

"Look — the way I feel now, I wouldn't care if I never saw another book as long as I live. But if anybody doesn't pay for a library book, you know what they do next?"

"No, what?"

"They send a letter home to your parents, that's what, asking them to pay for the book. Gosh, I wouldn't want my mother to be bothered like that, especially since she's told me about a thousand times not to read in the bathtub."

Billy could see that he had something there. "You'll have to earn it," he said. "How about mowing lawns?"

"I thought of that. But I've been everywhere, and the only place I could scare up anything was the Wallaces. Mrs. Wallace'll give me a quarter for it, and she says I can do it the rest of the summer."

"Then what're you crabbing about? Mow the Wallaces' lawn eight times, and you have your two dollars."

"*Eight times* — between now and Monday!" yelled Fats. "Listen, how fast you think the Wallaces' lawn grows, anyway?"

"Why didn't you say you had to have it by Monday? You better think fast."

Fats sighed. "I been thinking so fast my brains are overheated now. Besides, it makes me hungry." He went in the house to see what there was to eat, and Billy went along. There was half a loaf of bread, and a fresh comb of honey.

"Hey! Go easy on that honey," said Fats. "My mother says the price you have to pay for honey these days, she bets the farmers don't let the bees eat anything but orchids."

Billy tried to get some of the honey off the bread and back into the comb, which is practically impossible, as anybody knows that ever tried it.

"I got it!" he shouted suddenly. "Honey! Honey costs money!"

"Sure, sure," said Fats. "That's what I was just telling you."

"No, that's what *I'm* telling *you*! Didn't you ever read about wild bees, how they make honey

all the time, and store it in hollow trees, and
people get it out and sell it for loads of money?
Why, you can get bushels of honey that way, and
all for free."

"Oh, yeah?" said Fats. "Just grab a bee, I
suppose, and scare it into telling you where it
keeps its honey? No thanks."

"No fooling, it's simple. Just find some bees,
and follow them. You can have the first two
dollars we make, to pay for the book, and we'll
divvy up the rest. Come on!"

Fats still didn't think this was such a hot idea,
but he had to admit it was the only idea they
had. And anyway, they had finished up the bread
and about half the honey. So they went down
to the end of the street where it sort of petered
out into fields. Sure enough, there were about a
million wild flowers in bloom, and about a billion
bees buzzing all over them.

Billy said they should each pick a bee, and

watch it carefully; but the way they all buzzed around in circles, and nudged each other off the best flowers, Fats couldn't tell one bee from another. "Besides," he complained, "I don't like the expression on their faces."

"Never mind their faces," said Billy. "It's the *other* end you have to watch out for."

Suddenly a bee that Fats was watching zoomed straight up in the air, and took off for a patch of woods across the valley. Then other bees followed it. "There they go!" he yelled.

"Up and at 'em!" yelled Billy, and they were off, lickety-split, down the hillside. Following a bee-line was not so hard, because as soon as one bee left them behind, along came another, and another, all in a straight line. But after the first couple of minutes, it sure gave a fellow a crick in the neck.

But the worst part was after they got into the woods. Now a bee-line is just dandy for bees way up in the nice smooth air like that, but bees just don't give a hang how tough the going is down below. Billy and Fats followed those bees through

74

every bramble patch in the woods, and left pieces of skin and pants in all of them. They followed them across a wide squashy place where they sank in almost to their knees, and through thick tangles of vines that turned out, later, to be poison ivy.

They got deeper and deeper into the woods, and Fats got farther and farther behind. "Hey!" he croaked. "Wait up." His face was purple from the heat and running, and he was mud and scratches all over. "What makes you think these bees *have* a home?" he asked. "What if they're just house hunting?"

"Oh, come *on*," said Billy impatiently. He was in just about the same shape as Fats, but after all it was his idea, so he pretended not to notice.

And after a few minutes, he stopped and pointed. "There it is!" And sure enough, there it was; a high, half-dead sycamore, with a little hole in the trunk, way up, and bees going in and out.

"But where is the *honey*?" asked Fats, looking around as if he expected to find it all wrapped up.

"Inside the tree. Where do you think?"

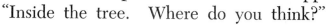

Fats lay down flat on the ground, and fanned his face. "All right. So it's inside the tree. Now let's see you get it out."

"Oh, we'll have to smoke out the bees," said Billy, very business-like. "We'll need axes and ropes and stuff. We'll just mark the tree today, so we can find it again."

"Axes. Ropes," said Fats in a hollow voice. "I thought you said this was simple." He sat up and looked around. "Hey, I'm lost. How do we get out of here? And don't say we can follow the bees back, because I wouldn't go back the same way for two million dollars. No, not even for two dollars, *cold cash*."

Billy pointed ahead, where the trees thinned out. "Let's try that way. I bet we come out on a road."

He started off, and Fats hauled himself up off the ground and followed, grumbling. They were just shoving through the bushes at the edge of the trees, and looking back over their shoulders to keep the top of the bee tree in sight, when it happened.

There was a skunk in those bushes.

Well, there are lots of people that think that a skunk is just terribly, terribly funny. But if you have ever noticed, they are always the ones that never had anything to do with one, personally. About the only thing you can say for a skunk is that it certainly takes your mind off your other troubles.

There were some farm buildings across a couple of fields, and that meant a road of some sort. Fats just headed for them without a word, but Billy had to make him stop a minute and line up the top of the bee tree with a couple of landmarks, so they could find it again.

They had to cross a chicken yard to get to the farmhouse and the road, so they climbed the fence and waded across, knee-deep in chickens, all clucking and squawking, that half-witted way chickens do. They were just climbing the fence on the other side to get out again, when a big black ugly dog came rushing at them, barking.

Then he got just close enough to get one good whiff of them, and you never saw a dog change his mind so fast, or look so foolish about it, either. He stopped barking right in the middle of a bark, with his mouth open and started backing away, stiff-legged.

77

A man's voice called, "Here, King! What is it, boy?" and the farmer came around the corner of the house, carrying a shotgun. King never even glanced at him — just kept right on backing up until he backed clear under the house and disappeared. And that was the last they saw of *him*.

"Hey, you!" shouted the man, pointing the gun in the general direction of Billy and Fats. "You come down off of that."

They came down, just as fast as they could, and Billy started explaining, "We were down in the woods —" when the man got a whiff of skunk, and started backing away, for all the world like the dog. In fact, Billy and Fats wouldn't have been surprised to see him double up and crawl in under the house with the dog. And they wouldn't have blamed him, either.

But he just said, in a sort of strangled voice, "I guess you have, at that." He set the gun down, and added, "Thought you kids might be stealing chickens, but I reckon you got other things on your minds right now."

"All we want to know is which way to Wherryville?" said Billy.

The farmer held a handkerchief up to his face with one hand, and pointed with the other. "Follow the dirt road half a mile, then left on the state road." He gave them plenty of clearance as they walked past, then asked, "What were you kids doing in my woods, anyway?"

"Looking for a bee tree," replied Billy over his shoulder.

"Say, there might be one, at that," he called after them. "Bunch of bees swarmed on me a couple of years ago, and got away. Been meaning to have a look —" But they were out of hearing, and traveling fast.

It was a silent trip. Nobody said a thing until they were nearly home, then Fats asked, "Didn't that man say those were *his* woods?"

"Yeah."

"Then if they were *his* bees —"

"Yeah?"

"You suppose — maybe it's *his* honey?"

"Yeah," said Billy. He left Fats at his gate, and went home.

And, if you will believe it, he was not allowed in his own house by his own parents, but hustled into the garage and told to take off all his clothes and throw them out the window. Then his mother passed him a bar of soap and the business end of the garden hose, and he had to work on himself for at least half an hour before she let him wrap in an old blanket and dash into the house.

Without anybody telling him to, he took five hot and cold showers, one right after the other. Then his mother came in and sniffed, and said she guessed it would have to do, but she sprinkled him with eau-de-cologne anyway. When he came down to supper, his father said he smelled like a barber shop, and that, on the whole, he preferred skunk. There was honey for supper, but Billy passed it up.

The next day he came out all over poison ivy, and it didn't make him feel any better when he remembered that Fats never took poison ivy.

It was a week before he got out of the house, and the first person he ran into was Fats.

"Guess what?" shouted Fats. "They burned all my clothes. Even my shoes."

"They buried mine," replied Billy with gloomy pride. "Say, what did your mother say about the pink book?"

"Oh, that. Nothing. I paid for it by Monday."

"Oh, yeah? What with?"

"The honey money."

"Listen, what are you talking about? That honey belonged to the farmer."

"I know it," replied Fats virtuously. "I just got worrying about the poor lost bees, and the poor farmer not knowing where they were, and honesty being the best policy and all. So I went right back the next day and showed him the bee tree. Say, he was tickled to death! Said he'd get the honey out all right, and his bees back, too.

"And then he handed me two-fifty. Just handed it to me, I never even asked him. So I paid for the book, and there's a quarter apiece left over, for us. How about coming down to Schultz's with me? They got a neat new flavor of ice cream called Honey Crinkle."

"*Honey* Crinkle? No, thanks. If it's all the same to you, I'll take vanilla."

81

WHAT HAPPENED?

Fats was in trouble. He needed two dollars by Monday. Why did Fats need the money?

His friend Billy finally got an idea for earning the money. They would find a hollow tree with honey stored in it. They would sell the honey. It would be easy. But how were they going to find the hollow tree?

Fats and Billy found the hollow tree with honey all right. But Fats and Billy found something else when they started home. Or rather something found them. What was it? What happened when they finally returned home?

Anyway, there was a happy ending. Fats made his two dollars and an extra fifty cents. How did he get the money?

THINK IT OVER

Remember the story about the bear who helped capture the bank robbers? We said the story was funny because unexpected and out-of-place things happened. This story is also funny. But it makes you laugh for a different reason.

Did you ever see, in a movie or on television, somebody get hit with a pie? Funny, wasn't it? We usually think it's funny when somebody gets in trouble that makes him look silly — especially if he is in no danger. Fats and Billy were in such trouble several times. What were the funny happenings in this story?

MUMPS

Elizabeth Madox Roberts

I had a feeling in my neck,
    And on the sides were two big bumps;
I couldn't swallow anything
    At all because I had the mumps.

And Mother tied it with a piece,
    And then she tied up Will and John,
And no one else but Dick was left
    That didn't have a mump rag on.

He teased at us and laughed at us,
    And said, whenever he went by,
"It's vinegar and lemon drops
    And pickles!" just to make us cry.

But Tuesday Dick was very sad
    And cried because his neck was sore,
And not a one said sour things
    To anybody any more.

83

TWO DINING ROOMS

Robin Palmer

The Barkington family were spending the winter at Grandmother's house in the city. They were very much pleased with the arrangement because they had been living in an apartment, where they never seemed to have enough room. There were *so* many Barkingtons — seven if you counted the new baby, and Mrs. Barkington felt that he always should be counted. So you see it was hard for them to fit into an apartment comfortably.

Besides, Grandmother needed to have them with her. She had been very ill, and though she was better now, the doctor said she must stay in her room and have her meals brought up on a tray. It was really the doctor who invited the family to come.

"Someone will have to look after your mother this winter," he said to Mrs. Barkington, "and she can't afford a nurse."

"She wouldn't *hear* of having one even if she could afford it," replied Mrs. Barkington with a laugh. "But there's no reason why I shouldn't take care of her. We can put our furniture in storage for a while." She picked up her hat at once and stooped to squint at herself in a mirror. She was a tall, thin woman with a dreamy look in her gray eyes. "Let me see," she went on, "the first of the month is on Monday. You can depend on us to be here." And without another word, she hurried home to pack.

Then the doctor went upstairs and told Grandmother what he had done.

The old lady was simply furious. "The very idea!" she cried. "I won't have people trying to run my life for me. How much rest do you think I'll get with five children in the house?"

"Oh, come now," said the doctor soothingly. "They're splendid children, you know they are, and a little noise isn't going to hurt you a bit. It's sweeping and dusting that you want to avoid."

Grandmother sniffed in a way that showed she was still very much annoyed, but the doctor wouldn't give in. So the following Wednesday (for Mrs. Barkington had been mistaken about the date) the whole family arrived, carrying suitcases, bundles, and baskets, and of course the baby.

They looked up at their new home as they climbed the brownstone steps. It was certainly not a pretty house, and it was exactly like its neighbors, which pressed so close on either side that they seemed to share the same walls. Nevertheless, the Barkingtons were proud to be moving in.

Mrs. Barkington was proud of the fact that the house had two dining rooms. "These days lots of people haven't *any* dining room," she said, "but Grandmother has two. What fun it will be to eat our meals in different places — quite like royalty, I think."

The first dining room was next to the kitchen. The second was upstairs, right over the kitchen, with a dumbwaiter to carry the dishes up and down. The Barkington children were proud of the dumbwaiter. It looked like a big wooden box with the front open, and it went up and down between floors the way an elevator does. When you wanted to send something upstairs, you put it on the dumb-waiter and pulled the rope. Up went the box to the second dining room. Patsy had already suggested that they should take turns send-ing up the dinner.

Patsy was the only girl Barkington, so she had a hard time keeping up with the boys. Some-times, when they wanted to tease, they called her Pigtail Pat, because she wore her dark hair in two short braids that just reached her shoulders. She was seven years old,

and she was right in the middle of the family.

Her two older brothers were Roddy and Jim, and her two younger brothers were Punch and Cornelius Junior. Punch was going on three, but the children called him the old baby because the new baby was really new.

"Leave the bags in the hall," Mrs. Barkington said, as soon as they entered the house, "and come right upstairs to see Grandmother."

She led the way to the old lady's room, calling out cheerfully, "Well, here we are."

"So I see," Grandmother answered.

There was a pause as she kissed them systematically. "Now then," she began, "I hope you children will enjoy it here, but don't forget that it's *my* house, and I expect you to take good care of it. Don't break things or move the furniture about, and please try to get your exercise out of doors."

"Oh, we'll be quite careful," Roddy assured her, "really we will." He took off his glasses and began polishing them vigorously. They didn't need polishing, but Roddy had only been wearing glasses for a week, so he cleaned them often.

"Now I'm going to pop right downstairs and make you a cup of tea," Mrs. Barkington said, "while Father and the boys go back to the apartment for the rest of our things. We couldn't quite carry all our clothes on one trip, and of course there were Jim's caterpillars."

"Eh?" cried the old lady.

Jim shuffled his feet and stared nervously at the rug. Oh, why did Mother have to mention him!

"Jim is very much interested in animals and bugs and things," Roddy hastened to explain. "He thought it would be fun to bring some caterpillars into the house and watch them build their cocoons, you know. So he went to the park and made a very good collection, and in the spring we'll have our own butterflies."

"For mercy sakes!" cried Grandmother. "What do the rest of you collect?"

"Oh, nothing alive," Roddy replied. "Just stamps and things."

"Well, that's a blessing," said the old lady. "The caterpillars can stay in the back yard."

Jim had been edging toward the door while

this conversation was going on. He muttered something about getting started and dashed down the stairs.

"Yes, indeed," Mrs. Barkington said, "you boys should be running along, and I must get the tea."

She left the room with the others trailing after her.

It was some time before Grandmother stopped reminding the children about taking care of her house and her furniture, but before long they were used to her, and she was beginning to get used to them.

One Saturday evening all the family except Father gathered in the kitchen to watch the preparations for supper. The baby lay in his basket in the middle of the floor, calmly sucking his thumb although Jim was jumping back and forth over his head. Jim was the sort of boy who hated to sit still. Roddy and Patsy perched on the edge of the table, while their mother fixed Grandmother's tray.

"Where do we eat tonight?" asked Roddy.

"Upstairs, I think," answered his mother. "It's SO much easier to send things up in the dumb-waiter. Oh, Punch dear, don't put the kitty's tail in your mouth. I'm sure it doesn't taste good. Will someone please take the cat away from Punch?"

Jim stopped jumping long enough to put the cat outside in the yard.

"NO! NO! NO!" shouted Punch.

His mother gave him a cracker.

"The new baby is a lot easier to take care of than Punch," Jim remarked. "Sometimes I wonder whether we really needed Punch in this family."

"Goodness me," exclaimed his mother, "as if we could do without any one of you! You used to be just like that when you were little."

Roddy chuckled. "A real nuisance, that's what you were," he said to his brother. "Boy, how you yelled!"

"I did not," Jim retorted. "Anyway, how could you remember?"

"I have an excellent memory," said Roddy. "And after all, I'm eleven and a quarter years old and you're only nine. Of course I remember." He slid off the table. "I hope there's enough to eat," he went on. "I'm as hungry as a bear. In fact, I'm as hungry as two bears."

He walked over to the stove and looked into the pots and pans. "Saturday night," he groaned. "Nothing but beans and apple sauce."

"AND bread and butter," said Mrs. Barkington emphatically. "Quite enough for anyone."

Roddy sighed and began to wipe the steam off his glasses. He was still rubbing them when his father came in.

Mr. Barkington worked at the zoo. He was a big, good-natured man with a deep bass voice. All the animals liked him.

"Hi!" said Roddy. "You're right on time."

Mr. Barkington smiled. "Hi, yourself," he replied. "Where do we eat tonight — upstairs?"

"So much easier," answered his wife. "Besides, we had lunch in the dining room down here. RODDY! For goodness sake! Not in there with all the food!"

Roddy was just putting the baby into the dumbwaiter.

"Easier to give him a ride upstairs than to carry him," he said.

92

"Sometimes it's better not to take the easiest way," his mother answered. "Give the baby to me. Father, you may carry Punch. Roddy, bring the high chair out of the first dining room. And Jim, don't forget the baby's basket."

With these words Mrs. Barkington sailed out of the room and up the dark stairs. The family followed her — all but Patsy. It was her turn to pull up the dumbwaiter.

When at last they were at the table, everyone began to talk at once. Punch banged his spoon on his high chair, and the baby started to cry. In the midst of all the racket, Mrs. Barkington cocked her head on one side like a bird.

"I hear something," she remarked.

"Is it rats?" asked Mr. Barkington. "Rats sometimes make a noise in the wall."

"If you would just be quiet," begged his wife.

"I hear it, too," said Patsy. "It does sound like rats."

"Oh, BOY!" shouted Jim. "I'll tame them. I've always wanted some tame rats. They're smart as anything. Is it rats, Mother?"

"Oh, no," said Mrs. Barkington, with a little cry of dismay. "Oh, dear me, NO! It's GRAND-MOTHER. She's banging on the wall. We must have forgotten her tray. Will you take it up, Roddy?"

Roddy grunted and left the room. In a few minutes he slid into his place again. "Grandmother thinks we are making a good deal of noise," he said. "She can hear us all the way up in her room."

"Can she really?" asked Mrs. Barkington. "It's remarkable what a keen sense of hearing she has at her age. You'd better shut the door."

Punch was sitting between his mother and Jim, but he was a little higher than Jim because he was in a high chair. Patsy sat across the table from them. Suddenly she noticed a roguish expression come over Punch's face as he looked down on Jim's curly hair.

"Look out, Jim," shouted Patsy. "Look out for Punch."

Jim swung around just in the nick of time. Punch had a spoonful of beans all ready to drop on his head.

Mrs. Barkington took the spoon away and went right on talking to Father. That was more than Punch could bear. He opened his mouth and yelled.

"Don't pay any attention to him," said his mother.

This was difficult because Punch had a powerful voice and he was putting all his strength behind it. His face grew red. He closed his eyes tight and let out roar after roar.

"You know," Mr. Barkington said, "I believe Grandmother is right. It IS noisy in here." He had to shout to make himself heard.

"Let's all be quiet while we count a hundred," suggested Mother.

"But Punch can't count, and he's the noisiest of all," said Jim.

"It reminds me of the monkey house at the zoo," shouted Mr. Barkington.

That gave Patsy an idea. "Punch," she cried, between his yells, "we're going to play a game."

Punch was rather tired of crying by that time, so he stopped to listen.

"The first one to speak, laugh, or even squeak," said Patsy, "is a monkey."

There was a dead silence. Mrs. Barkington smiled. She always liked to play games, and of course the children did, too. They made signs to one another across the table. Punch looked at them thoughtfully and wondered what was going on. He was not old enough to understand.

Then Mr. Barkington picked up a bottle of tomato sauce for his beans. He shook it vigorously to be sure it was quite well mixed.

POP! The cork shot out of the bottle and flew clear to the ceiling. So did a lot of the sauce. It made a large red spot.

"Oh, my goodness," cried Mr. Barkington. "Oh, my GOODNESS!"

Everyone began to laugh.

"Daddy's the monkey," said Patsy. "Daddy's the noisy one this time."

"He certainly is," agreed Mrs. Barkington. She looked up at the spot.

"WHAT will Grandmother say?" asked Roddy.

Father sighed. "I was just wondering that myself," he said.

"Don't you worry," laughed Mrs. Barkington. "She'll speak sharply and then forget all about it. That's the way she is. Besides, when she has guests she can use the other dining room. I always knew it was a good thing to have two."

WHAT HAPPENED?

Grandmother wasn't sure she was going to like having all seven Barkingtons in her house. But the seven Barkingtons were glad to be in the big house. Why, it even had two dining rooms. Where were the dining rooms?

Saturday night the Barkingtons decided to use the dining room served by the dumbwaiter. What is a dumbwaiter?

Roddy decided to use the dumbwaiter for something besides food. What was his plan?

Just after they sat down to dinner, Punch decided to have a little fun with a spoonful of beans. What did he try to do?

Father brought the dinner to an end. The Barkingtons were all playing a game at the dinner table. How did Father end the game?

THINK IT OVER

It takes much give and take to get along in a family, in the neighborhood, and at school. The Barkingtons are a good example of a big family where each member knows he will not always get his own way. What do you do in your family to settle arguments fairly? What else do you do to help the family get along together?

In many ways getting along with other boys and girls is even harder than getting along with brothers and sisters. For one thing, there isn't always someone like Father or Mother to settle an argument in neighborhood or schoolground play. What do you do in your neighborhood or on the school playground to settle arguments fairly? What else do you do to help boys and girls get along together?

THE KIND MOON

Sara Teasdale

I think the moon is very kind
   To take such trouble just for me.
He came along with me from home
   To keep me company.

He went as fast as I could run;
   I wonder how he crossed the sky?
I'm sure he hasn't legs and feet
   Or any wings to fly.

Yet here he is above the roof;
   Perhaps he thinks it isn't right
For me to go so far alone,
   Tho' Mother said I might.

A HIKE IN THE WOODS

Carolyn Haywood

Peter, age eight, and his adopted brother Penny, age six, have many good times with their family. This part of the story tells about a weekend in the woods.

In the morning, Peter and Penny and Daddy set out to explore a stream. Mother packed their lunch basket. There were frankfurters that they were going to cook over an open fire. Peter wore the frying pan dangling from a strap that he wore over his shoulder.

On the opposite side of the lake was the mouth of a stream. Daddy said he thought that would be a good stream to explore. So they climbed

into the rowboat and rowed across. When they
landed, Daddy made the boat fast by tying it to
an old tree stump.

The three explorers walked along the bank of
the stream. It was about twelve feet wide and
the water was as clear as crystal. The pebbles
and stones on the bottom looked as though they
had been scrubbed, they were so clean. Here
and there were big rocks, and whenever it was
possible, the boys crossed the stream by stepping
from rock to rock.

"One of you fellows will drop the lunch in the
stream, if you don't watch out," said Daddy.
"You had better let me carry the basket."

Peter handed over the basket to Daddy. The
three swung along, whistling.

Sometimes the trees and bushes grew so close to the stream that one could hardly find a foothold, but they pressed on because it was all new and exciting.

Finally they came to a place where the bank was very high above the stream. Here they had to walk carefully. Daddy lifted a heavy branch so that Peter and Penny could pass under it. As he lifted it, the basket on his arm tilted and the package of frankfurters flew out of the basket, the paper opened, and they fell in a shower down to the stream.

"Oh, Daddy!" cried Peter and Penny together. "The hot dogs!"

The three looked down as the frankfurters dove into the water. They watched them float downstream — one, two, three, four, five, six, seven, eight, nine of them — all pink and plump.

"Well!" exclaimed Daddy. "Guess they'll be cold dogs forever now."

102

"Oh, Daddy!" cried Penny. "Now we'll have to eat the rolls with nothing in them but mustard."

"Isn't that the limit!" said Daddy. "I am so sorry."

Peter and Penny looked very gloomy indeed as they continued on their way. Before very long, they were close to the stream again, and there were stepping stones so that they could cross the stream. When they reached the middle of the stream, Penny said, "Look, Daddy. What makes those little splashes in the water and the ripples?"

Daddy looked where Penny was pointing. "Oh!" exclaimed Daddy. "That must be a school of trout."

The ripples came nearer and under the surface of the water there appeared to be a dark shadow. As it came closer, Penny could see that what looked like a shadow was a school of fish.

To the surprise of the boys, as the fish passed, Daddy quickly reached into the water and when he pulled out his hand he had a trout in it.

"Quick, Peter!" he said. "Take the rolls out of the basket."

103

Peter took the rolls out of the basket, and Daddy put the fish in. He put a rock on top of it to keep it from jumping out. Then he looked down in the water again. In a moment, he had another trout. He popped it into the basket and put in another stone.

Peter's and Penny's eyes were as round as saucers. "Oh, Daddy!" said Penny. "Do you think you can catch another one?"

"I'll try," replied Daddy.

They waited, holding their breath. Soon Daddy plunged his arm into the stream again, and once more he pulled up a fish. "That water is just like ice," he said.

"How did you ever learn to catch fish that way, Daddy?" asked Peter.

"It's a trick an old Indian taught me when I was a boy. He lived near my grandfather, and there was a stream there with a great many trout."

"It's some trick!" said Penny.

"Well, now we have our lunch, haven't we, Daddy?" said Peter.

"You bet we have," replied Daddy. "A much better lunch than we lost."

"Isn't it time to eat?" asked Penny. "I'm hungry."

"Well, let's get started, anyway," said Daddy. "It will take us a little while to build the fire and get going."

The boys started to gather sticks for the fire, and Daddy set to work to clean the fish. He opened them up with his knife and washed them in the stream.

When the boys had gathered enough sticks, they built the fire. Before very long, it was burning well. When there were enough red embers, Daddy put some butter in the frying pan. When it was sizzling, he laid the three fish in the pan.

"Oh! Willakers!" cried Penny. "Isn't this exciting?"

"Real surprise party, isn't it?" said Daddy.

"Smells wonderful," said Peter.

Then suddenly, Penny cried out, "We haven't any forks. How are we going to eat the fish?"

Peter and Daddy laughed. "Penny certainly is civilized, isn't he, Daddy?" said Peter.

"He certainly is," replied Daddy. "I guess he wants fish-knives and forks with pearl handles."

They all laughed and Daddy lifted the golden brown fish from the pan and placed each one on a plate. At first, they were too hot to touch, but they soon cooled. Peter, Penny, and Daddy ate a delicious lunch and they didn't put mustard on their rolls.

When they had finished, Peter held up his ten fingers and said, "What! No finger bowls!"

And Daddy called out, "Minnie! The cut-glass finger bowls, please."

106

The boys laughed.

Then Daddy said, "'Smatter with Minnie?"

"Fell in the stream, I guess," said Peter.

"In that case, I guess we'll have to wash in the stream," said Daddy.

They all went, laughing, to the stream.

Afterwards, they made certain that the fire was out. Then they packed the soiled dishes into the basket and started off again. "I think we had better be getting back to Mother," said Daddy.

"But we haven't found any beaver dams," said Penny.

"No," said Daddy, "but perhaps the beavers haven't been building dams lately. Maybe we can come again, and next time we will find one."

"Oh, Daddy, do you think we can come again?" asked Peter and Penny in one breath.

"Maybe so," said Daddy.

They retraced their steps, crossing and recrossing the stream, until they reached a bend in it.

As they rounded the bend, there came into view a log that lay partly across the stream. There, snuggled against the log, were — one, two, three, four, five, six, seven, eight, nine hot dogs. They looked very forlorn and out-of-place.

Daddy saw them first, and he threw back his head and laughed a great big laugh. When he pointed them out to the boys, they all laughed very hard.

They walked out on the log and looked at the plump, pink weenies. "Let's take them home," cried Penny. "They're just as good as new. The water is so clean and cold. Don't you think it is all right to take them home, Daddy?"

"Sure!" said Daddy. "Gather them up."

The boys picked them all up and wrapped them in some paper napkins that were in the basket.

When they reached the mouth of the stream, they were all pretty tired. The little boys were glad to get into the rowboat and have Daddy row them across the lake. They ran up from the landing and into the cabin, shouting, "Oh, Mother! What do you think? We brought the hot dogs back."

WHAT HAPPENED?

Penny was a funny name for a boy. But he was all boy, just as his brother Peter was. Peter and Penny really enjoyed the hike with their father. For a while though, it looked as if they wouldn't have much food. What happened?

Daddy saved the day. He didn't have any fishing pole or line or hook, but he caught fish all the same. How did he do it?

On the way home Daddy looked into the stream and laughed. He saw some small objects in the water. There they were resting comfortably against a log. What were these objects?

THINK IT OVER

It's hard for most fathers to find time to spend with you. Fathers work hard all day. At night they often like to read the newspaper and talk a little to Mother.

Perhaps your own father doesn't always feel up to playing with you. Even on weekends there are so many things for Father to do he may not often be able to have fun with you.

Maybe there's something you could do to help, though. Could you try to be home most nights when he arrives? Your happy greeting will help him after a hard day. Could you hang up his coat and hat for him? He'll be glad for these little special services. What else could you do to show Father you look forward to his coming home?

On weekends could you take over some of Father's jobs so he'd have more time to be with you? What could you do?

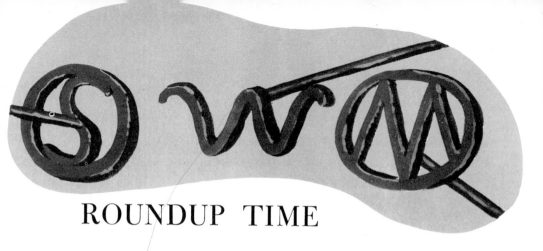

ROUNDUP TIME

Sanford Tousey

Tommy was on a visit to his great-grandfather who had sold his Kansas farm and moved farther west to the "Circle X" ranch where there was more room for his cattle to graze.

His great-grandfather, whom he called "Grandy," for short, had given Tommy a cowboy suit and a "two-gallon hat." The chaps that he wore to protect his legs were of real bull-hide and his tall hat with its broad brim was of the same kind of felt that the cowboys wore.

"Grammy," his great-grandmother, made cookies and pies for him and gave him all the preserves that boys like so well.

At first he had had to ride a gentle old horse named "Prince," but recently Grandy had given him a pony of his own called "Lightning." When

Lightning was younger he had been one of the speediest ponies on the ranch. He could still go fast enough for Tommy, and he knew all the tricks that a good cow pony should know.

A cowboy named Slim had been showing Tommy how to use his rope.

"When you're roping a horse afoot," said Slim, "don't whirl the rope 'round your head like you do when you're roping cattle from horseback. Let it trail behind you and then throw it straight from off the ground. Ride by on Lightnin' an' I'll show you."

Tommy rode off a way and came galloping back. Slim held the noose in his right hand and the coil of rope in his left. As Tommy went past, Slim threw the noose forward with a single movement and Lightning's neck was encircled by it. Lightning knew enough to stop at once when he felt the rope around his neck. Experience

had taught him it was no use to fight once the loop had settled.

There were some old ponies running around in the corral, and for days Tommy practiced on them until he was able to rope them.

Then Slim showed him how to guide Lightning without pulling on the reins.

By a slight touch of the rein on the neck he could make the old cow pony turn away from the pressure. Slim had Tommy ride Lightning out on the range to show him how the horse would follow a galloping steer.

By the time Tommy had learned all these tricks the day of the spring roundup had arrived. Tommy had been hearing about this for days, and he could hardly wait for it to start because Grandy had promised to let him go along with the cowboys.

There were to be four cowboys, besides Tommy,

113

from Grandy's ranch. Nine other ranches each
sent three or four cowboys, and every cowboy
brought along eight horses. So there was a big
bunch of horses in the band that had to be
watched by the "wrangler" and Tommy, who was
to be "wrangler's helper."

Grandy said, "Tommy, you'll need an extra
pony for this job. It's hard work and not all fun.
I've told Slim to let you have Chick for your
second pony, when Lightning gets tired." Chick
had a white star on his face, while Lightning had
four white stockings.

Two ponies! This was more than Tommy had
expected. And Chick was a good pony, too.

Over in the corral the horses were milling
around, and as Tommy came up, Lightning poked
out his nose for a friendly rub.

114

Tommy walked over near the big gate where the cook was straightening out the chuck box, getting ready for next morning's early start. The chuck box was the big box, like a cupboard, at the rear of the chuck wagon, in which the food was carried.

Besides the chuck wagon there were the bed wagon with its big tarpaulin to cover the cowboys' bed rolls, and the wood wagon which carried the wood and water for the cook.

Tommy went to bed early that night. It seemed as though he had hardly fallen asleep when the call came to get up. It was barely daylight when he walked out to the corral. A friendly cowboy went in and roped Lightning for him. Tommy soon had the saddle on and was ready to go. Each wagon had four broncos hitched to it. The

115

cook was driving the chuck wagon and when the men had his horses hitched up he shouted, "Give me the ribbons!" as they handed him the reins.

Slim had been chosen captain of the roundup, and Tommy felt proud that his best friend among the cowboys was in command.

The ranch gate was opened, the captain led the way, and the three wagons, with their broncos excited and prancing, followed. After them came the big band of horses in a cloud of dust, driven along by the cowboys. And Tommy on Lightning was one of them.

They rode for several miles until they reached the creek. Here the wagons stopped, and Slim started out with his men to work the day's "circle" and bring in the cattle —"critters," the cowboys called them.

Slim led the bunch to a high spot of ground up the creek and sent the boys out in pairs. The pair with the best horses was sent out farthest to ride the biggest "circle"— which meant that they had to travel around the rim of a large imaginary

116

circle and gather in all the "critters" they saw.
Inside their circle two more cowboys were doing
the same thing in a smaller circle, and so on.

The easiest job fell to the pair that had the
smallest circle near the center. When each pair
of cowboys had gathered all the cattle in their
territory, they started to drive them towards the
"cutting ground" near the chuck wagon.

That morning before Slim had left with the
cowboys he said to Tommy, "You just watch the
wrangler and do whatever he does. You'll soon
catch on."

So when Tommy saw the wrangler start to drive
the "saddle band" (as he called the herd of ponies)
across the creek where the grass looked greener,
he mounted Lightning and helped drive them
over. If one of the ponies took a notion to leave
the band and wander off, Tommy headed old
Lightning toward the "bunch quitter," and the old
pony turned him back. The wrangler had to go
and hustle some wood for the cook, so he was
glad to have Tommy look after the saddle band
while he was away.

When the wrangler was ready to put up the rope corral that acted as a temporary fence, he called to Tommy. They dragged the heavy rope out of the wagon and set it up. When the cowboys came back and wanted fresh horses it was easier to rope them in this corral than running loose.

The cook was very busy getting the grub ready for the return of the cowboys, but he knew how hungry a boy gets who rises before sun-up and rides all morning. So he gave Tommy a slice of bread and butter with some molasses on it. To Tommy at this time it tasted better than a slice of his own mother's chocolate cake.

He had scarcely finished when the wrangler yelled, "Here they come!" All Tommy could see was a great cloud of dust over the far hills. It came closer and closer and finally he could make out the cattle as the cowboys drove them toward the cutting grounds. There were hundreds in the herd. The cowboys rode their tired ponies into the rope corral and took off their saddles. Then they roped and saddled fresh ponies and started "cutting out" the calves that had to be branded.

Tommy rode over to where a fire had been started to heat the branding irons. Each calf to be branded was roped by a cowboy on horseback. It was thrown to the ground and held by two

119

men called "flankers." Then it was branded on the left hip with a hot iron. A mark was made that never wore off.

Each cow, calf, or steer must have a particular mark on it that showed who owned it.

Cattle thieves, called "rustlers," would sometimes steal the cattle and rebrand them by changing the first brand. Some of the brands looked like this:

And this is the way they changed the brand on Grandy's cattle:

Tommy got off Lightning and went over to help tend the fire. But first he dropped the reins of his horse's bridle so that they dragged on the ground. A cow pony is trained to stand wherever his reins are dropped.

As soon as the branding was finished the cowboys got their tin cups and plates and ran for the chuck wagon where the cook was yelling, "Come and get it!"

The cook had an enormous spoon, and he dished each man an ample helping of beans and of stew from the big pots. Then every cowboy helped himself to a cup of coffee and sat down to finish his meal. It was a tired bunch of men that crawled into their "soogans" that night and slept on the ground.

WHAT HAPPENED?

Tommy was glad to be able to help in the spring roundup. How was Tommy going to help?

Driving the "saddle bands" and turning back the "bunch quitters" was hard work. What kind of work was it?

Tommy was very interested in the branding of the cattle. He saw each animal marked with Grandy's brand. Tommy helped take care of the fire. He got off Lightning and let the reins drag on the ground. Why did he do that?

After a good chuck-wagon dinner, Tommy and the cowboys crawled into their "soogans" to sleep. What do you think "soogans" are?

THINK IT OVER

Tommy learned much about the West through his visit to the Circle X ranch. Perhaps the West was not just as he thought it would be. Have you visited places only to find they were quite different than you had imagined? What was different? The people? The countryside?

Tommy also learned much about the life of cowboys. Surely he learned some things about cowboy life he didn't know. Have you learned about some of the jobs people have? Maybe your father and mother have talked to you about their work. What part of their jobs would be new to most people?

PIRATE STORY

Robert Louis Stevenson

Three of us afloat in the meadow by the swing,
  Three of us aboard in the basket on the lea.
Winds are in the air, they are blowing in the
    spring,
  And waves are on the meadow like the waves
    there are at sea.

Where shall we adventure, today that we're
    afloat,
  Wary of the weather and steering by a star?
Shall it be to Africa, a-steering of the boat,
  To Providence, or Babylon, or off to Malabar?

Hi! but here's a squadron a-rowing on the sea —
  Cattle on the meadow a-charging with a roar!
Quick, and we'll escape them, they're as mad as
    they can be,
  The wicket is the harbor and the garden is the
    shore.

THE ROCKING MONKEY

Mary Graham Bonner

Nine-year-old Billy Dart lived in Four Corners with his parents, his sister Maggie, and Grandma Dart. He had a dog named Mootch, and two pet bear cubs, named Strawberry and Jam.

Billy's mother was pleased with him. He got up early in the morning and took Mootch for a long walk, remembering to bring home wild flowers and ferns. Mrs. Dart was going to have a tea party, and she wanted the house to look attractive. Now, too, Mootch would be willing to lie on the kitchen porch for the rest of the day. Billy was going to play baseball with his friends. They were taking their lunches with

"The Rocking Monkey" reprinted from *Something Always Happens* by Mary Graham Bonner, by permission of Alfred A. Knopf, Inc. Copyright, 1946, by Alfred A. Knopf, Inc.

them, and were coming home late. Grannie and Maggie were busy making sandwiches. Maggie was going to wear her best blue dress and pass the refreshments to the guests. Everything had been perfectly planned.

"I hope your side wins," Billy's mother told him, as he picked up his baseball bat and mitt.

"I'll sock that old apple, Mom."

"What?"

"Furzey Orr, who's pitching for the Lions, is my cousin."

"Why, Billy, he's no relation, though they are very old friends. Mrs. Orr is coming here today."

Billy laughed.

"He means," Maggie proudly explained, "that he's always able to get hits off Furzey."

"Oh," Mrs. Dart answered absentmindedly, for

she was thinking of further preparations for the party. "Maggie," she continued, "will you please brush the front porch and dust the chairs?"

Maggie fetched the broom and duster.

"Grannie," she called as soon as she had gone outside, "shall I leave your shawl on your rocking chair, or shall I bring it in?"

"Leave it there," Grannie answered. "If I go on the porch to chat with someone later it may come in handy. It's always cool in the afternoon on that side of the house."

The Lions and Bears were playing a double header. The first game was a runaway for the Bears for the first six innings. They had scored ten runs, and Billy had hit a homer with the bases loaded. The Lions had also made many errors. In fact the Bears thought the game was in the bag, and grew careless, while the Lions got their batting eyes in the seventh. To Billy's shame an error was chalked up against him when

he lost a fly ball in the sun. The Lions scored five times in this inning and twice in the eighth. In the ninth, two of the Lions got walks, but then Nat, who was pitching for the Bears, tightened and struck out the next three boys. The game was over.

They had a swim in the river before lunch. Afterward they talked over the game until it was time to return to the field for batting practice. Then the two pitchers warmed up. The game started.

For three innings not a hit was made, and only one boy reached first base on a wild throw. It certainly looked like a pitchers' battle.

As the Lions were about to go out into the field in the fourth, a hurdy-gurdy was heard in the distance.

"Do you suppose there's a monkey with it?" someone asked.

"Let's go and see," another suggested. "We can come back and begin the fourth inning afterward."

"Sure," the rest agreed. They could finish their game later — particularly when the score was tied — for a hurdy-gurdy hardly ever came to Four Corners.

They ran in the direction from which came the sound of the wheezy music. There stood an organ-grinder, surrounded by a few children and several older people. Perched on top of the organ was a monkey, wearing a red cap and tattered red velvet jacket. With one hand the monkey slapped his pocket in which coins jingled, while the other was outstretched for more.

The organ-grinder looked pleased at the approach of so many boys. He had been doing none too well visiting such small places as Four Corners, and was disgusted with his monkey and the organ-grinding business.

The boys produced a few pennies, and the monkey grabbed for them in his hot little hand, shoving them into the pocket. Then he took off his cap and made a low bow, while his master

jerked him down to the ground. The monkey did an awkward dance as though the hot street hurt his feet.

"This sidewalk is baking," Nat observed. "The monkey's feet aren't tough enough to stand it."

The organ-grinder scowled, and then made an attempt to smile; but it was not a pleasant smile. . . .

"Go and have a rest. We'll take care of the monkey," Nat offered.

"Sure," said Billy. "My house is the nearest — and he can sit in our front yard where it's cool. He'll also be safe from Strawberry, Jam, and Mootch."

The organ-grinder hesitated. He did not understand all that Billy said, but he was tired. He wanted to sit by the river and go to sleep. . . .

"O.K. I'll be back in coupla hours. Mind you don't steal the monkey or I'll set police on you."

"That's all right," Andy grinned. "We only have one policeman here, and he's our friend."

"Also my dad," Furzey chuckled. "Your monkey will be safe."

The organ-grinder took the pennies out of the monkey's pocket and put them in his own. "You be here in coupla hours sure, see?"

The boys nodded, as he walked away. . . .

Some of the children followed the boys as they took the monkey to the fountain in the square and gave him a drink of water, and bought a banana for him at the fruit store. The monkey neatly peeled off the skin and ate the banana hungrily. Then Billy carried the monkey home, tying his rope to one of the posts on the porch.

Nat took off the monkey's jacket and cap and put them on the steps. They left him sitting on the cool grass. His eyes were almost closed. He looked very weary.

"There'll be plenty of time to finish the game before we have to return him," Furzey said.

"It's a good thing you seldom see monkeys with organ-grinders now," Nat remarked, as they were on their way to the field. "Sometimes I suppose

130

they're treated all right, but it's too hard a life for them."

As soon as they resumed their game they forgot about everything else. The Bears wanted to make it two straight, and the Lions were fighting to break even. It remained a pitchers' battle until the ninth inning when each side threatened with two of the Lions getting hits and two of the Bears getting on through an error and a walk.

The Bears were helpless in their half of the tenth. Then, to everyone's surprise — including his own — Furzey hit a homer. The Lions were always lucky in an extra-inning game. It was even-Stephen for the day.

"We'd better get the monkey before we swim," Billy suggested, "though I do wish we didn't have to return him to his owner."

"You'd start a zoo if you had your way about it," Andy said. "Your mom probably thinks Mootch, Strawberry, and Jam are enough."

"I don't suppose any of our families would let us keep a pet monkey," Nat added mournfully. "Even if we had the money to buy him."

Carrying their bats and mitts they walked to Billy's house, but as they approached the gate they heard a terrific clatter. There stood the tea party guests shrieking and shouting, while on the front porch sat the monkey rocking back and forth in Grannie's rocking chair. He actually had her shawl around his shoulders.

At the same moment the front door opened and Mrs. Dart, Grannie, and Maggie appeared, for they had heard voices and had wondered why the guests did not come right in. Mrs. Dart thought she must be having a most peculiar dream. Maggie giggled, and Grannie was too astonished to speak.

"Where in the world did that monkey come from?" Mrs. Dart finally gasped. Then she saw Billy and his friends at the gate.

"Billy Dart! Don't I have one afternoon of peace?"

"I forgot about your party, Mom. The monkey's only resting."

"Resting!" she cried. "Take him away. This moment."

Grannie was laughing now as she looked at the monkey rocking in her chair, and wearing her shawl.

"I hope," she said, as their friends came up the

steps, while Billy lifted the monkey to his shoulder, "that none of you sees any resemblance between the monkey and the elder Mrs. Dart!"

"Mom!" Maggie tugged at her mother's elbow. "Can't I go with the boys?" She saw Nat picking up the monkey's jacket and cap.

"Certainly not," her mother whispered.

The guests were all chattering at once. As the boys left they could not help overhearing some of the remarks.

"You can imagine my surprise when I saw the monkey," exclaimed Mrs. Wallace. "I was the first to arrive, and while I didn't suppose he was dangerous I felt it was better to wait for the others."

"I couldn't believe my eyes," added Mrs. Sidney. "I knew you had bear cubs in your back yard, but I didn't think I'd see a monkey on the front porch."

"We should have taken the monkey to our place. Mom left early to do some errands before she went to your mother's party," Andy said.

"Too late to think of that now," Furzey remarked.

Billy carried the monkey to the corner where they were to meet the organ-grinder. While they were waiting, a car came along in which sat Mr. Dart and a stranger.

"There's my son," Mr. Dart shouted, and the man who was driving stopped the car. "I mean the boy," Mr. Dart added, wondering how Billy had ever managed to find a monkey.

The boys grinned and Mr. Dart continued, "Fellows, this is Mr. Ashburn. He's the director of a large city zoo, and has been on a camping trip up North."

"Monkeys are my specialty," Mr. Ashburn said. "Where did you get this one?"

The boys told him. . . .

"I wish he didn't have to stay with the organ-grinder," Nat said.

"He'd be much happier in my zoo," agreed Mr. Ashburn.

"Couldn't you —" began Nat, but he did not finish what he had hoped to say, for they saw the organ-grinder coming toward them.

"Your monkey's getting old," Mr. Ashburn told the organ-grinder. The man . . . turned to the boys.

"What you kids done to my monkey?"

"They've taken excellent care of him. I merely thought," Mr. Ashburn continued, "that the monkey won't be able to work for you much longer. . . . I'll buy your monkey if you don't ask too much for him."

The organ-grinder's eyes gleamed. He was tired

135

of tramping around the country, and the monkey had grown feeble. With a little money he could return to the town where his grownup children lived. There he could sit in the sun and do nothing. . . .

"He cost me plenty money," the organ-grinder said finally.

"I know exactly what he's worth — or rather what he isn't," and Mr. Ashburn named the sum he was willing to pay.

The organ-grinder hesitated for a moment. He knew it was a fair price. Then he said, "I let you have the monkey."

He started off toward the station, grumbling that he had not been paid enough. . . .

"Golly, what a stroke of luck for the monkey," Nat exclaimed. "You don't suppose the man will go and buy another one?"

"I'm not afraid of that," Mr. Ashburn replied. "Business isn't worth it. But I don't believe," he continued, turning to Mr. Dart, "that I'll have time to stop off and meet your wife. I'm due

136

down the line in another hour, and the monkey must have some warm milk and go to bed."

Mr. Ashburn drove off. Until he was out of sight the boys waved, and the monkey waved his cap.

"He seems better already," Nat said.

The guests had left when Billy and his father got home.

Grannie was sitting on the front porch, wearing her shawl and rocking back and forth.

"I'm Grannie," she chuckled, "in case you're not sure."

Maggie and her mother came out the front door.

"We had a most successful party," Mrs. Dart said. "In spite of everything," she added, looking at Billy.

"To tell you the truth," Mr. Dart admitted, "I, too, forgot about your party. A Mr. Ashburn stopped in the bank, and I was planning to bring him to the house to meet you when we saw Billy, the boys, and the monkey."

"It would have been a trifle awkward today," Mrs. Dart told her husband, "and he probably wouldn't have enjoyed a ladies' tea party."

"Mr. Ashburn likes monkeys," Billy said.

"Oh my," said Billy's mother.

"But next time," Grannie turned to their father, "try not to forget when we tell you we're having a party. How can we expect Billy to remember when you don't?"

"Grannie, you're swell," said Billy.

"At my expense," laughed his father.

"Well, it did turn out to be a lovely tea," Mrs. Dart smiled happily. "I think they all had a good time."

"Come, Mag. Let's feed Mootch and the cubs," Billy said. Maggie joined her brother.

"What a family we've got!" Billy exclaimed.

WHAT HAPPENED?

Billy's team, the Bears, had an easy time in the first six innings of the opening game. But the Lions scored many times in the seventh and eighth innings. What was the final score?

The organ-grinder and his monkey broke up the second game for a while. The organ-grinder was tired. So was the monkey. What did the boys do to help them?

The second game went for nine and a half innings without a score. Then Furzey of the Lions broke up the ball game. What did he do?

When the boys returned to Billy's house, they

139

heard a big noise. It seemed to come from the porch. And sure enough the monkey was the cause of it all. What was he doing?

Mr. Ashburn knew what to do about the monkey. He talked to the organ-grinder. The organ-grinder finally agreed. What was to happen to the monkey?

THINK IT OVER

The organ-grinder had a hard life. Probably he had always been poor. Very likely he would rather not be an organ-grinder. Sometimes he may not have been as kind to his monkey as you think he should have been. Why do you think he might have been unkind at times?

Of course, not everyone acts the same way even though the same things happen to him. Another organ-grinder might have been very kind to his monkey. He might have been kind even though he was poor and didn't like his job.

Suppose you once knew a fourth-grade boy with red hair who became angry easily. You wouldn't say then that all red-headed boys get angry easily. No two people ever act just alike. In our country we never say that we are sure someone will act badly just because someone else like him did once. Can you think of any time when you almost made this mistake? Or do you know someone else who made this mistake?

140

UNIT THREE

HAPPY STORIES
OLD AND NEW

A
HALLOWEEN
STORY

Elizabeth Dillingham

Once upon a time a big orange pumpkin was growing just outside a stone wall, far off in a field, all alone. The farmer had gathered all his pumpkins and stored them carefully in his great barn. But no one knew of the big orange pumpkin growing just outside the wall, all alone. The big orange pumpkin was lonely.

"I wish I belonged to someone," he said.

"Miaow, miaow! I do, too," cried a little black pussy cat, stretching herself and jumping down from the stone wall where she had been sleeping.

"It will soon be winter," said the big orange pumpkin. "Let's go find someone to belong to."

"Yes, let's do," said the little black cat, eagerly. "I want to belong to a little girl with a sweet face and shining eyes."

"And I," said the big orange pumpkin, "want to belong to a jolly boy who whistles and sings when he works. Let's hurry right away to find them."

"Yes, let's do," said the little black cat.

Off they started — the big orange pumpkin rolling and tumbling along, and chuckling to himself as he went, and the little black cat

"A Halloween Story" from *The Rabbit Windmill* by Elizabeth Dillingham. Copyright, 1930, by The John C. Winston Company.

pitpatting along on her soft little cushions, purring because she was happy.

On and on they went, over the fields and through the woods. It began to grow cold, oh, so cold, and dark, too. The little black cat shivered as the wind whistled through the trees.

"See here," said the big orange pumpkin, "you can't sleep outdoors tonight. What shall we do?"

Just then they saw a man coming along the path with a bundle of wood on his back.

"Ho, Mr. Woodcutter!" cried the pumpkin, "have you a knife?"

"That I have," said the merry woodsman. "What can I do for you, my fine fellow?"

"Just cut off a piece of my shell where the stem is, and scoop out some of my seeds, if you please," said the pumpkin.

No sooner said than done.

"There, my little black pussy cat," said the pumpkin, "when you wish to sleep tonight, you may curl up inside and be as warm as a sunbeam."

"But will you not go home with me?" asked the woodsman.

"Have you a little girl with a sweet face and shining eyes?" asked the little black pussy cat.

"Have you a jolly little boy who whistles and sings when he works?" asked the big orange pumpkin.

145

"No, ah, no," said the woodsman, "but I have a pig and some hens."

"Then we will go on," said the pumpkin, "but thank you, kindly."

So on they went, and on, until the stars began to shine. Then the tired little pussy cat curled into her hollow nest, put on the cover, and went to sleep.

In the morning they went on again, but before long it began to rain. The pussy cat's soft fur was soon very wet.

"You poor little thing," said the big orange pumpkin, "curl inside your house and I will trundle you along."

"But it's so dark inside, and I couldn't see where we were going," cried the pussy cat, holding up a tiny, dripping paw.

"Windows!" cried the pumpkin. "Of course, windows! How stupid of me! Wait here under this fence, my little friend, until I come back."

Then off he hurried across the road to a carpenter's shop.

"Ho, Mr. Carpenter!" cried the pumpkin, "have you a knife?"

146

"That I have," said the jolly carpenter. "What can I do for you, my fine fellow?"

"Just cut some windows for me, if you please."

So the carpenter took a sharp knife and cut four windows — just like a face he made them — two for eyes, one for a nose, and one for a mouth, and he laughed as he did it. When he finished the mouth, the pumpkin laughed, too.

"Ha, ha, ha!" cried he. "What a relief to have a mouth to laugh with! Ha, ha, ha!" And he laughed all the way back in the rain to where the little shivering pussy cat was waiting.

And she laughed, too, and climbed inside her coach, and put on the cover.

So on through the rain they went, and on and on. Just as dark was drawing near they came to a wee, brown house by the side of the road. In the yard was a little boy picking up chips and putting them into a big basket. He whistled as he worked, and then he began to sing:

> "If wishes were horses,
>   Then beggars might ride;
> If turnips were watches,
>   I'd wear one by my side."

Then the door opened, and a little girl with a sweet face and shining eyes stood on the threshold.

"What *do* you wish, John?" she called.

"Oh," laughed the boy, as he came in with the chips, "I wish I had a pumpkin for a jack-o'-lantern for this Halloween."

"And I wish I had a pussy cat to love," said the little girl.

"This is the place for us," whispered the big orange pumpkin; and he rolled up to the door, bumpity-bump.

"Look, John!" cried the little girl, "here's your jack-o'-lantern! The fairies must have sent it. Isn't it a beauty?"

"There's something inside," said John, snatching off the cover, and out jumped a tiny black pussy cat, straight into the little girl's arms.

"Oh, oh!" they cried.

And when Mother came home in the dark, a jolly jack-o'-lantern with a candle inside was shining out of the window at her, and close beside it sat a little black pussy cat.

WHAT HAPPENED?

The woodcutter was the first to help. The cat needed a place to sleep. The pumpkin asked the woodcutter to fix up a place. What did the woodcutter do?

The carpenter was the next to help. The cat couldn't see where the pumpkin was going. The carpenter fixed that quickly. What changes did the carpenter make?

The cat and the pumpkin finally found the place they were looking for. How did they know it was the right place?

THINK IT OVER

The cat and the pumpkin wanted to belong to someone. People are the same way. They like to feel they belong somewhere. Fathers and mothers like to feel they belong to each other and to their children. Boys and girls like to feel they belong to their fathers and mothers and to their brothers and sisters.

Fathers and mothers like boys and girls to show how they feel about their family. Some boys plan birthday surprises. Some girls fix Sunday breakfast. What could you do to show your mother and father you like to belong to them? What could you do to show your brothers or sisters you like to belong to them?

THANKSGIVING DAY

Annette Wynne

Brave and high-souled Pilgrims,
   You who knew no fears,
How your words of thankfulness
   Go ringing down the years;
May we follow after;
   Like you, work and pray,
And with hearts of thankfulness
   Keep Thanksgiving Day.

"Thanksgiving Day" reprinted by permission of the publisher, J. B. Lippincott Company, from *For Days and Days* by Annette Wynne. Copyright, 1919, by J. B. Lippincott Company.

150

WHY WILD ROSES HAVE THORNS

Frances Jenkins Olcott

Long, long ago, Wild Roses had no thorns. They grew on bushes. Their stems were smooth, and their leaves were green. Sweet-smelling pink blossoms covered the bushes. Oh! they were beautiful to see!

But they made such delicious eating that the rabbits, and other forest creatures, nibbled the pink petals and green leaves. Sometimes they even ate up the bushes. By and by there were only a few Rose Bushes left in the whole world.

Well, the Rose Bushes that were left met together to see what they could do about it. They decided to go and find Nanah-booz-hoo and ask him for help.

Now this Nanah-booz-hoo was a strange fellow. He had magic power and could make himself as tall as a tree or as small as a turtle. He could not be drowned or burned or killed, and he had a very bad temper when he was displeased. He was hard to find, for sometimes he was an animal and at other times he was a man.

But the Rose Bushes decided to look for him. They hurried away on the back of a wind that they hired to carry them. And as they went along, they asked every tree and animal they met, "Have you seen Nanah-booz-hoo?" And all answered, "No."

The Rose Bushes flew on and on. By and by they met a little animal that said, "Nanah-booz-hoo is in a valley among the mountains, where he is planting and taking care of a flower garden."

The Rose Bushes were delighted to hear this, and told the wind to blow them to that valley, and it did. As they drew near the flower garden, they heard Nanah-booz-hoo shouting, for he was very angry. The Rose Bushes were dreadfully frightened, and hid among the balsam trees. But they soon learned why Nanah-booz-hoo was so angry.

Some weeks before he had planted a hedge of wild roses around his garden. When they were covered with spicy pink blossoms, he had gone away for a few days. When he returned he found that the rabbits and other creatures had eaten up his hedge of wild roses, and trampled down all his flowers.

Now, when the Rose Bushes knew why Nanah-booz-hoo was shouting with rage, they left their hiding place, and a puff of wind blew them straight to Nanah-booz-hoo's feet. He was surprised to see them, for he thought that all rose bushes had been eaten up. But before he could say a word, they told him their troubles.

Nanah-booz-hoo listened, and after talking things over with the Rose Bushes, he gave them a lot of small, thornlike prickles to cover their

153

branches and stems close up to the flowers, so that the animals would not be able to eat them. After that Nanah-booz-hoo sent the Rose Bushes to their home, on the back of the wind.

And ever since that day all wild roses have had many thorns.

WHAT HAPPENED?

Nanah-booz-hoo was a person made up by an Indian tribe. He had strange powers. What kinds of things could he do?

Nanah-booz-hoo liked roses. He was angry when the rabbits ate his hedge of roses. What did he decide to do?

THINK IT OVER

For hundreds of years people have made up strange people and magic animals to explain things they didn't understand. Some of these stories still are believed by people in different parts of the world. Do you know any stories like that? What did these stories try to explain?

You might like to try making up stories to explain some modern magic. Could you write a story to explain the magic of television? Perhaps you would rather tell a story about jet airplanes. What other modern magic can you tell a story about?

154

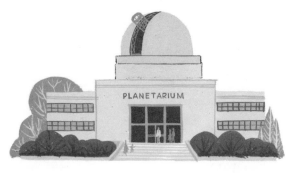

ROCKET
TO THE MOON

Frances Frost

Jean and David are starting on a trip to the
moon — pretend, of course! Their father is
going to wait for them at the Planetarium.

"We ought to be ready for the blast-off at any
moment now," the guide said.

Jean reached out and seized David's hand and
held on tight.

"Earth Dispatcher to Crew! Earth Dispatcher
to Crew! Fasten all space ports! Fasten all space
ports!"

There was a bang as all the space ports were
slammed shut.

Another voice chanted, "Engineer to Pilot and

Co-pilot! Engineer to Pilot and Co-pilot! Prepare for blast-off. Prepare for blast-off!"

High up in the rocket ship David saw suddenly the blue-lit cockpit of the ship and the dark forms of the pilot and co-pilot sitting before their instrument panel where red lights flashed on and off.

Then came the pilot's calm slow voice, "Pilot to Earth Dispatcher! Pilot to Earth Dispatcher! Code number X–F–4! Code number X–F–4! Ready for blast-off! Dial set! Clear area! Clear area! Five-four-three-two-one-zero! Rocket away!"

There was a terrific roar of the jet engines. The rocket left its cradle and shot into space.

Jean clung to David's hand, and both of them leaned hard against the backs of their seats.

The inside shutter of a square space port, high

in the rocket, opened. There ahead of them, through the meteor-proof plastic window, was the Moon, very small. But as they sped toward it, the Moon grew steadily bigger. Its pale gold color turned to gray plains and sharp dark shadows. It seemed to David that they were going to crash right into the rough, sharp-toothed mountain ranges. There was a great flash of light that blinded them.

David gasped and couldn't believe his eyes. They were in a crater on the Moon! Jagged peaks rose straight up around the edge of the crater. The peaks were lit by the strange yellow light of the Sun that hung in the south. The vast sky was black and filled with stars, even though the Sun was shining. And there, straight ahead above the Moon peaks, was the globe of the Earth, turning slowly on its axis.

David was shaking with excitement and delight. He glanced at Jean, and she was gazing at the

far-off Earth with her mouth open in astonishment.

"We made it!" he said. "We've landed on the Moon!"

The guide announced in an excited voice, "We have arrived on our satellite, the Moon! That red ball in the southern part of the sky that looks like the Moon is really the Sun."

The children gazed fascinated at the millions of stars over their heads. The stars were much clearer and larger than they look from the Earth because there were no clouds or air to hide them or blur them.

The guide pointed out the biggest stars and named them. Then he showed them the Milky Way, the great river of stars that stretches across the sky.

David said, "There's the Big Dipper."

And Jean said, "There's the Little Dipper and the North Star!"

They knew that the North Star, in the Little Dipper, is the star that never rises or sets as seen from the earth but is always shining in the northern sky to guide travelers on land or sea.

"Come on," said David. "Let's walk around and see what the Moon is like."

"Okay," said Jean through her walkie-talkie.

They started out to explore.

"Don't go far from the rocket ship!" warned the guide. "The long night that lasts two weeks on the Moon will be coming soon. The Sun is getting closer to the west right now. And when it goes down, it sinks very quickly. We haven't brought a big enough load of oxygen on this first trip to the Moon to stay for a long time. Have fun, but don't get out of sight of the ship!"

"We won't!" answered David.

There was no blue sky, and it was dark except for the strange light from the Sun.

"The Earth looks a lot bigger from here than the Moon does from the Earth," Jean said.

"About four times bigger because it is bigger," David said. "Hey, I feel awfully light, do you?"

"Yes," said Jean and she took a hop, skip, and jump. "My goodness! Look at how high I went! I can't jump that high on the Earth! I wish I'd brought my jump rope! If I could do this at home, I could beat all the other girls at school."

David had an idea. "At home my record for standing broad jump is five feet. Wait till I see what I can do here."

"Wow! That was thirty feet, easy! I remember why — that's because gravity on the Moon is only one-sixth of what it is on the Earth. So we can jump six times as high or far."

"This is fun!" exclaimed Jean. "Let's play leapfrog!"

They had a wonderful game until they were both out of breath from laughing. Then suddenly, Jean disappeared.

David was horrified. "Jean!" he shouted. "Where are you? Come back here! Jean!"

She giggled but he couldn't see her. Then she walked out of the black shadow of a low peak.

Shadows on the Moon are much darker than shadows on the Earth because there is no air to scatter the sunlight. She had just hidden in a Moon shadow to tease him.

"Don't you ever do that again!" he scolded. "Want to scare me to death? What would Mom and Dad say if I lost you on the Moon?"

"Wouldn't this be a wonderful place for hide-and-seek?" she asked.

David picked up a small piece of rock from the dry, dusty, gray ground and started to toss it. It went flying over his head.

"Oh, boy!" he said. He picked up another piece of rock and tried to pitch a curve. But it was no good, because it is air pushing against a ball that makes it curve. He thought a baseball game on the Moon wouldn't be much fun, but

he did wish he could throw that far on the Earth.

Jean was bending over a big rock, and she picked it up as easily as if it were a doll. "Look at how strong I am!" she bragged.

"No, you aren't," David answered. "You aren't any stronger than usual. It's just that gravity isn't holding the rock down the way it does on the Earth. Because the Moon hasn't as much gravity as the Earth has."

She gave the rock a toss, and it went a good distance. "Let's play leapfrog again," she said.

But at that moment their walkie-talkies began to crackle. The guide's voice commanded, "Return to Rocket! Oxygen running low! Return to Rocket!"

"Oh, phooey," said Jean. "Just when we were having fun!"

"Never mind," David told her. "We'll come back to the Moon some other time. Obey orders."

161

The engineer's voice called loudly, "Oxygen running low! Oxygen running low! Everybody into Rocket! Everybody into Rocket!"

The steel beams and struts of the rocket ship were about them again. David and Jean braced themselves for the blast-off toward the Earth.

The rocket went dark. In the pilot's cockpit blue and red lights flashed on and off.

The pilot's voice called, "Pilot to Engineer! Pilot to Engineer! Code number X–F–4! Dial set!"

"Pilot and Co-pilot," came the answer. "Prepare for launching! Prepare for launching!"

"Ready for launching," replied the pilot. "Ready for launching! Five-four-three-two-one-zero! Rocket away!"

The top space port opened, and David saw the Earth coming toward him, growing bigger and bigger. And he thought swiftly, "Oh boy, I like the Earth!"

The rocket ship slipped sideways as it hit the Earth's atmosphere, and the pilot shouted, "Prepare for landing! Prepare for landing!"

They were right smack on top of the North American continent when a bright light flashed. David opened his eyes to the skyline of the city. "Whew!" he said and shook himself to make sure he was home.

He nudged Jean. "Hey," he said, "we're home on Earth again. We've got to find Dad, remember?"

"Uh-huh," she said vaguely. Then she came to. "Dad!" she yelled. "Will he be waiting for us?"

"Sure," said David, laughing. "It's still Saturday here."

Dad was sitting on the bench at the top of the stairs just as he said he would be. He looked up from his book and his eyes and his grin were real.

"Hello, kids," he said. "Have a nice voyage?"

Jean flung her arms around his neck.

David grinned back at Dad. Gosh, it was good to see him! He couldn't say anything for a minute. Then he managed, "Fine voyage, Dad!"

"I thought you'd like it," said Dad. "Jean, let go. Want to choke me?" He stood her off and gave her a little shake. "It's all right," he said. "You're back on Earth. You weigh sixty pounds on Doctor Bill's scale."

Jean backed up and gazed at Dad.

"I'd rather," she said firmly, "weigh sixty pounds and be here on Earth — for a little while. But some day I would like to visit Saturn and see how those rings work. They look like a dancing lady's skirt."

Dad chuckled. "Well, maybe we can do something about that right now. Would you two like to sign up for the first official Interplanetary Tour?"

David didn't have to think twice. "You bet, Dad! Where?"

"Downstairs on the first floor," Dad said.

They trooped down, hand in hand.

"I'll get the application blanks right here at the inner ticket office," said Dad.

164

"You make them out and turn them back in, and they'll be kept on file until the first space ship is ready."

David took his yellow blank over to the big iron-black meteorite. He put it down on the granite base and dug in his pants pocket for his stub of a pencil.

He printed his name and address. When it came to checking the boxes for Moon, Mars, Jupiter, Saturn, he thought hard.

"Start with the Moon," he said to himself, "and keep going."

He checked all four voyages. It would be like playing leapfrog in space — if he got to the Moon, he could get to one planet after another.

"What did you check, Jean?" he asked.

"The Moon," she said, "and Saturn. I hope they hurry up and build that rocket ship. But right now, I'm hungry!"

"So am I," said David.

"Turn your applications in at the window," said Dad, "and we'll all have ice cream outdoors."

The late afternoon sun was lovely and warm, and the sloping grass was soft and green. They sat in the grass to eat their ice cream.

David and Jean agreed that it was nice to be back on the Earth. But they both told Dad that it was the best vacation voyage they had ever had.

WHAT HAPPENED?

The rocket ship flew straight to the Moon. The Moon was no longer a gold ball as David and Jean came close to it. What did the Moon look like?

Jean and David decided to walk around on the Moon. It wasn't at all like walking on Earth. What was different?

When Jean and David returned to Earth, Dad was waiting. He said they could sign up for another tour. Where could they go on this new tour?

THINK IT OVER

Have you read any other stories about space travel? Or have you seen short plays in motion pictures or on television programs? One way writers make their stories good is by using unexpected happenings. Were any of the space stories you read or saw full of unusual happenings? What was different about the stories?

A good story also gives a very clear picture of the characters. Of course, these characters are not always people you would ever see. The people might be very different from any on Earth. But the story makes the people seem so clear you know exactly how they look. Did any of the space stories you read or saw have people you can still remember clearly? What were these people like?

166

GRANDPA DROPPED HIS GLASSES

Leroy F. Jackson

Grandpa dropped his glasses once
In a pot of dye,
And when he put them on again
He saw a purple sky.
Purple birds were rising up
From a purple hill,
Men were grinding purple cider
At a purple mill.
Purple Adeline was playing
With a purple doll.
Little purple dragonflies
Were crawling up the wall.
And at the supper table
He got crazy as a loon
From eating purple apple dumplings
With a purple spoon.

THE LITTLE DRAGON

Constance Savery

There was a little dragon, quite nice and tame. His name was Augustus, and he lived with his father and mother in a cave with colored icicles hanging on the roof.

As the little dragon could not fly very far, he often had to stay at home in the cave on the hillside, coiled round three times, watching the people who passed in the valley far below. He liked watching the boys and girls and market folk, but when the prince rode by in golden armor on his coal-black steed, the poor little dragon nearly cried.

"I wish I were a prince," thought he. "How fine I should look in that flashing armor on that black horse! Oh, I do wish I were a prince!"

"Well, so you are a prince," said the old gypsy woman who had come softly up the hillside to the

"The Little Dragon" reprinted by permission of the author.

entrance of the cave. "But you are under a spell cast by those wicked dragons who are pretending to be your father and mother. They turned their dragon son into a prince, and they turned you into a dragon and took you to live in their cave."

"But why did they do it?" asked the little dragon.

"Ah, it's a fine thing to have a prince for your son," laughed the gypsy woman. "Mr. and Mrs. Dragon always were ambitious."

"Can't I undo the spell?" said the little dragon.

"You might," said the gypsy. "Take a crystal bowl, fill it with powdered sea shells steeped in elderberry cordial, and drink deep. That should serve you."

Then the gypsy woman hobbled away. She did not mean to tell an untruth, but unfortunately she had made a sad mistake in thinking that Mr. and Mrs. Dragon had cast a spell on their little Augustus. They had done no such thing.

The little dragon felt angry and important. He puffed out his chest at the thought that he was really a prince who owned the white, shining palace down in the valley. "I will undo the spell at once," he said.

169

So he waddled down to the shore and gathered sea shells and pounded them with his mother's flatiron and steeped them in elderberry cordial. Next he poured the mixture into a crystal bowl, and last of all he drank it. He also swallowed the flatiron quite by mistake, which was perhaps the reason why the spell was not undone. For he was still a little dragon.

When the gypsy woman came again, the little dragon was very cross with her.

"Your spell was worse than useless," said he. "And Mother was dreadfully vexed about her flatiron."

The gypsy woman was sorry for him. "I will tell you other remedies," she said.

And she gave him seven more spells for undoing spells, but none of them was any good. The little dragon slept on young green nettles for nine nights, and ate toadstools gathered from thirteen fairy rings, and washed in sea foam mixed with May dew, and drank four potions, each more horrible than the last — but nothing would turn

him into a prince. At last he grew tired of trying spells. One day the prince rode past the cave on his black horse, and at once Augustus pounced on him and dragged him inside.

The prince was not expecting to be pounced on. He was so much taken by surprise that he did not even try to fight the little dragon.

"Now I've got you, wicked creature!" said Augustus. "You're not a prince at all. You're the son of the dragons that live in this cave. I am the real prince under a spell."

"Absurd!" said the prince, as bravely as he could.

"It isn't absurd," said Augustus indignantly. "Take off your armor and your clothes. I am going down to my palace. You must stay here."

The prince struggled hard, but Augustus was the stronger of the two. He tore away all the beautiful golden armor the prince had on and most of the prince's clothes. And then Augustus dressed himself for his arrival at the palace.

It took him three hours to dress and don his

armor. Everything was so small that he had to fasten himself together with pieces of string and many safety pins. The prince sulked in a corner, refusing to help.

As soon as Augustus was dressed, he locked the door of the cave behind him, left the key in the lock, and marched down to the palace. The courtiers and servants. were just setting out in search of their gallant prince, who had not returned from hunting in the hills. The sight of the little dragon made them run away screaming.

"Do not be afraid, my friends," said Augustus. "I am your unhappy master under a spell."

So they came timidly up to him, and he was led into the palace.

Meanwhile the prince sat in the cave with colored icicles, wondering what would happen when Mr. and Mrs. Dragon came back from their ride through the air. At midnight he heard the beating of their great wings.

172

"And pray, who are you?" said Mr. Dragon in surprise.

"I am the prince of this country," answered the young man. "Your son dragged me into this cave and robbed me of my armor and my clothes, saying that he was the true prince. A gypsy woman had told him so. He has gone to my palace to take possession of it."

"So that's what was the matter with Augustus!" said Mrs. Dragon. "I could see that silly child had something on his mind, but I couldn't find out what was troubling him. He thinks he's a prince under a spell, does he? Ha, ha, ha!"

"I should like to go home now," said the prince politely.

"You can't," said Mrs. Dragon. "Not like that! It is beneath your dignity to go to your palace in the few rags Augustus has left you. I would make you some new clothes if I could," she added kindly, "but unluckily I am not good at sewing. My claws always catch in the stuff."

"You had better stay with us until Augustus returns," said Mr. Dragon. "He'll come home sooner or later. He's not cut out for a prince. He, he, he! Have some supper?"

So they lighted a fire and cooked a fine supper for the prince and lent him Augustus' bed. And he lived in the cave on the hill.

As for Augustus, he sat on a tight, uncomfortable, golden throne, dressed in glorious robes. All day long, tailors were running sharp pins into him as they tried on his new court clothes. At night he slept in the state bed, which was so much too small for him that he often rolled out of it with a terrible bump on the floor. And at mealtimes he never had enough to eat. When he cleared the gold and silver dishes, his courtiers whispered to one another, "What a greedy appetite his Highness has!"

One day he was sitting by himself in the gardens of the palace, a lonely little dragon. His subjects believed that he was their prince, but they were always afraid that a prince under a dragon spell might be tempted to snap. So they left him alone.

He looked up, and there stood the gypsy woman.

"How are you getting on?" she inquired.

"Not very well," said the little dragon.

"The prince is getting on very well indeed," said the gypsy. "He likes his life in the cave. At night your mother and father take him out treasure-hunting. He sits on your father's back, holding his scaly wings. They went to the mountains of the moon last night to gather moonstones. And you should see the emeralds he brought back from the shores of the sea that no man knows!"

"Oh!" said the little dragon.

"Then they come back and make a huge fire of dried ferns and pine cones and sea wood, and your mother cooks the supper. Plum porridge! Great big platefuls!"

"Oh!" said the little dragon. "Oh!"

"And when the dishes are washed and shining dry, your mother and father sing to him — scales and catches and snatches!"

"Oh!" said the little dragon. "Oh, oh, oh!"

And he asked anxiously, "Does my mother — Mrs. Dragon, I mean — does she like him better than me?"

The gypsy woman only laughed.

Late that night Mr. and Mrs. Dragon heard a whimpering and sniffling outside the cave. They looked out and saw Augustus. In his claws he held clothes and a suit of armor for the prince.

"Oh, Mother, let me in!" he cried. "I want to come home. I don't believe that gypsy woman spoke the truth. I would rather be a dragon than a prince."

175

"You are much better fitted to be a dragon than a prince, Augustus," said his mother severely. "Come in at once, and don't let me hear any more nonsense."

So Augustus came in and sat down. The prince began to dress himself in his splendid clothes and glittering armor. He looked every inch a prince as he buckled on his sword. Then he drew it from the scabbard and bade Mr. Dragon kneel.

"I wish to reward you for your services," he said.

Mr. Dragon knelt as well as he could for his tail.

The prince struck him lightly on the shoulder and said, "Rise, Sir Dragon."

Then he said good-by rather coldly to Augustus, climbed onto Sir Dragon's back, and was swiftly borne home to the palace. Lady Dragon went, too, carrying the moonstones and emeralds.

Augustus stayed at home and washed the dishes, after he had eaten all that was left of the good supper. Then he crawled into his large bed, saying to himself, "It's better to be a dragon than a prince. There's no place like home."

And the little dragon went happily to sleep.

WHAT HAPPENED?

Augustus wanted to be a prince. But he was only a dragon. The old gypsy woman promised to help. She told him to drink a special drink. What was in it?

Then the prince came along. The little dragon changed places with him. What was his life like after he became a prince? Did he ever see his mother and father again?

THINK IT OVER

It's fun to imagine being somebody else. You could be a jet pilot. You could be a television star. Perhaps you would rather be a great doctor. Maybe you would choose to be a fine singer. What is your choice? What would you do?

Of course, you don't have to be somebody who is grown up. You might rather be another kind of boy or girl. You might be a French boy. You might be a Japanese girl. What is your choice? What would you do?

177

MOTHER CHRISTMAS

Rose Fyleman

"My dear," said Mother Christmas, "it's no use. You can't go."

"Nonsense," said Father Christmas. "Of course I shall go. I've never missed yet. The children would never get over it."

"Then let *me* go," said Mother Christmas. "It's absurd for you to think of it with a cold like that on you. I can manage perfectly. After all, it was I who packed up all the presents, and I know exactly where to take them."

"And how are you going to manage the reindeer, I'd like to know, with all those telegraph wires about?" said her husband. "No, my dear, it's a man's job. I shall be all right. Mix me a hot drink, and I'll have five minutes' snooze by the fire before I start."

"Mother Christmas" by Rose Fyleman from *Number Two Joy Street*. Reprinted by permission of the publishers, Appleton-Century-Crofts, Inc.

Mother Christmas said no more, but there was an odd gleam in her eye as she mixed Father Christmas' glass of hot lemon and water. It's my belief she put something more than lemon into the hot water; however that may be, it certainly made him very sleepy. The five minutes' snooze lengthened into ten — fifteen — twenty. Mother Christmas was moving about the room very quietly and softly. She wrapped herself up in all manner of woollies, and at last put on her husband's great red coat and hood all trimmed with white fur, and stole quietly out of the door.

Plup, plup, plup — there was a noise of light hoofs flying over the snow.

Plup, plup, plup — softer and softer it grew. At last it died away.

Father Christmas still slept by the fire.

When he woke up it was quite dark, and it didn't take him many minutes to realize what had happened. He hurried to the reindeer shed — empty.

The snow was falling thickly. He was terribly upset. What was to be done? He had no other

sleigh and no other reindeer, and of course it was impossible to follow his wife down to earth on foot.

Finally he decided to ring up the Fairy Queen. She was always so kind and helpful.

"Please, your Majesty," he said when he had got through, "I'm nearly distracted. My wife insisted upon taking out the Christmas presents because I had such a cold, and I'm so afraid she may get lost, or stuck somewhere."

"Dear, dear," said the Queen. "Hold the line a minute while I tell the head of the look-out department to put on his million-horse-power-wireless-radio-telescope-spectacles in order to see where she is." In a minute or two came news.

"She's caught on some telegraph wires, and the reindeer and the sleigh are all tangled up in them. He can see them quite plainly. What would you like me to do?"

"Oh dear, oh dear," said poor Father Christmas. "I'm afraid the only thing to do is to cut the wires, and the wire cutter is in the toolbox under the seat of the sledge. She'll never think of that."

"Would you like me to send her a message?" said the Queen.

"Oh, your Majesty, if you *would* . . ." said Father Christmas.

So the Queen sent down a messenger at once with instructions about the wire cutter.

Mother Christmas was in a dreadful tangle. She simply could not get out, and the reindeer were kicking and plunging in a most troublesome way.

Large snowflakes were falling. They fell onto
Mother Christmas' hair and nose and spectacles.

She put up her hand to brush one off her ear.

"Hi," said a tiny voice. "You mustn't treat me
like that. I'm a Queen's Messenger."

Mother Christmas took off her spectacles and
wiped them and put them on again.

A tiny, dapper, little person sat on the rail of
the sleigh. He really did look rather like a
snowflake in his snug white cap and ulster, but
he was very much alive.

"The wire cutter's in the toolbox under the
seat," he said, and was off like a flash. He
wanted to get home to bed, I expect. And so
Mother Christmas got back safely after all, and
she had delivered all the presents, too. You may
guess what a welcome she received from her
husband and what a lot the reindeer had to talk
about to one another before *they* went to sleep.

"There must have been a terrible gale last night," people said on Christmas morning. "Quite a lot of telegraph wires are down."

The head of the listening department in Fairyland heard them and told the Queen what they said. How she laughed!

THINK IT OVER

Some people think that stories of space ships or fairy queens or dragons are silly. You may have thought so yourself, sometimes. Yet old people and young people all over the world continue to like this kind of story. They like stories about tiny people and giant people. They like stories about people you cannot see at all. They like stories about strange animals. They like stories about wonderful lands far away.

Maybe that's why "Mother Christmas" is such a good story. It's a story about people you can't see at all. It has animals that soar through the air, and Father and Mother Christmas come from a land far away. Is there anything else that makes "Mother Christmas" a good story?

183

A–CAROLING ON CHRISTMAS EVE

James S. Tippett

On Christmas Eve
We always meet
For singing carols
On our street.

We sing the carols —
Three or four —
In front of every
Neighbor's door.

And through the opened doors
We see
Each neighbor's
Lighted Christmas tree.

"A-Caroling on Christmas Eve" from *Counting the Days* by
James S. Tippett. Copyright, 1940, Harper & Brothers.

LONG, LONG AGO

ANONYMOUS

Winds thru the ol - ive trees soft - ly did
blow, Round lit - tle Beth - le - hem,
long, long a - go. Sheep on the
hill - side lay whit - er than snow,
Shep - herds were watch - ing them long, long a - go.

Then from the happy sky
    Angels bent low,
Singing their songs of joy,
    Long, long ago.

For in a manger bed
    Cradled we know,
Christ came to Bethlehem,
    Long, long ago.

185

THE OLD HOUSE

Hans Christian Andersen

There in the street stood a house that was almost three hundred years old. Flowers and lines of poetry were carved into the wood above every window. On the end of the rainwater pipe was a dragon's head. The water was supposed to run out of its mouth. But now there was a hole in it, and the water never even reached the mouth.

All of the other houses in the street were neat and modern, with large windows and strong walls. You could tell they would have nothing to do with the old house. They thought, "How long is that old thing going to stand there? It makes our street look terrible. And that dreadful brass railing! It makes one feel ashamed!"

At a window in the house across the street sat a boy with bright shining eyes and fresh rosy cheeks. He liked the old house best of all those on the street.

186

When he looked across at it, he could imagine the strangest pictures. He could see the street as it had been in the old days. Yes, to him that was indeed a house worth looking at!

A very old man lived in the old house. He wore old-fashioned clothes and an old-fashioned wig. Every morning a servant came to clean the rooms and to buy the food. Otherwise the old man lived all alone. Whenever he came to the window the boy waved to him, and the old man waved back. In this way the young boy and the old man became friends.

One day the boy heard his parents say, "The old man over there has plenty of money, but he is very lonely!"

Next Sunday the boy wrapped something in a piece of paper. When the servant who bought the food for the old man came by, the boy said to him, "Look, sir, will you please give this to the old gentleman across the street? I have two tin soldiers. This is one of them, and I want him to have it because I know he's very lonely."

The man looked very pleased as he took the tin soldier across to the old house. Later he brought back a message asking the boy to come over and pay a visit. Happily the boy went across to the old house.

The brass railing shone brighter than ever — one would think it had been especially polished for his visit. Then the door opened.

In the hall were pictures of knights in armor and ladies in silken gowns.

Then the boy entered a room where the walls were covered with flowered paper.

There were big soft chairs with high backs. "Sit down! Sit down!" they seemed to say.

At last the boy came into the room where the old man sat waiting for him.

"I thank you for the tin soldier, my young friend," he said. "And I thank you also because you came to see me."

The pendulum of a big clock swung slowly back and forth. The hands turned slowly. Everything in the room slowly became still older.

"My mother and daddy say," said the boy, "that you're very lonely."

"Oh," the old man answered, "I have many happy thoughts, and now I have you to visit me, too. I'm really very happy."

Then he took a picture book down from the shelf. There were pictures such as the boy had never seen. What a wonderful book that was!

The old man went into the next room to get some jelly, apples, and nuts. Yes, the old house was a wonderful place. But suddenly the tin soldier cried, "I can't stand this any longer. It's so lonely here! I can't stand it any longer! Things here aren't the way they were over at your house, where your father and mother spoke so pleasantly, and you and the other children made such happy noises. I simply can't stand it here any longer!"

"You mustn't be so sad," said the boy. "I think it's fun here."

"But," said the tin soldier, "I tell you I can't stand it!"

"Well, you must!" replied the little boy.

Then the old man came back smiling, and with the most delicious jelly and apples and nuts! So the boy forgot about the tin soldier.

He went home, happy and pleased. Weeks passed before the boy went over to call again. It was just like the first time, for in that house one day was just like another.

"I can't bear it!" cried the tin soldier. "I've even been shedding tin tears. This old house is too sad! I'd rather go to the wars than stay here. At least that would be a change! I just can't stand it!

"Tell me, do you still sing on Sundays? Tell me about your little sister Mary! And how is my friend, the other tin soldier? I imagine he's happy enough! Oh, I can't stand it any more!"

"You were given away to the old gentleman as a present," said the boy firmly. "And you must stay here! Can't you understand that?"

Now the old man brought in a box in which there were many things — coin boxes and large, old-fashioned playing cards. Then the old man

opened the piano. It had pictures painted on
the inside of its lid, and it was squeaky when the
old man played it! He hummed a little song.

"I'm going to the wars! I tell you I'm going
to the wars!" the tin soldier shouted, and he
threw himself down to the floor.

What had become of him? The old man
searched, and the little boy searched. The tin
soldier was gone; they couldn't find him anywhere.

"I'll find him," said the old man, but he never
did. There were cracks in the old floor, and the
tin soldier had fallen through one of them.

That day passed, and the little boy went home.
Time passed, and one day the old man died.

In the spring the old house was torn down.

"Thank goodness," said the other houses. "That
ugly old house is gone."

At last a fine house was built there. It had
large windows and strong white walls and a little
garden in front of it.

Many years went by, and the boy had grown

up now to be a man. He had just been married and, with his pretty wife, came to live in the new house where the garden was.

He was standing beside her in the garden one day while she planted a wild flower. She placed it in the ground and pressed the earth around it with her fingers. Ouch, what was that! She had pricked herself. Something was there, pointed straight up in the damp dirt.

It was — just think — the little tin soldier! The same one that had been lost in the old man's room. He had rested for years in the ground, waiting.

The young wife wiped the dirt from the tin soldier, first with a green leaf and then with her pretty handkerchief which had such a wonderful perfume that the tin soldier woke as if from a dream.

Then the young man told his wife all about the old house and the old man and the tin soldier.

"How very lonely he must have been!" she sighed.

"Terribly lonely!" repeated the tin soldier. "But it's wonderful not to be forgotten!"

WHAT HAPPENED?

How was the old house different from the other houses on the street? The other houses did not like the old house. Why didn't they like it?

The boy felt sorry for the old man who lived all alone in the queer old house. The boy decided to give the old man a present. What was it?

The old man liked the present. He asked the boy to come and see him. On the first visit the boy and the old man ate jelly and apples and nuts. On the second visit the old man showed him a box. What was in the box?

The toy soldier fell through a crack in the old man's house. The old man never did find the soldier. But many years after the old house was torn down, the toy soldier was found again. Where was he found? Who found him?

THINK IT OVER

The old man was lonely because he lived all alone. But sometimes older people are lonely even when they live with others. Perhaps their own children have grown up. Maybe they live where there are no children. Most older people enjoy having children as friends. Suppose you found an older person who did not have any children as friends. How could you show that you would like to be a friend?

193

I'LL WEAR A SHAMROCK

Mary Carolyn Davies

Saint Patrick's day is with us,
   The day when all that's seen
To right and left and everywhere
   Is green, green, green!

And Irish tunes they whistle
   And Irish songs they sing,
Today each Irish lad walks out
   As proud as any king.

I'll wear a four-leaf shamrock
   In my coat, the glad day through,
For my father and mother are Irish
   And I am Irish, too!

"I'll Wear a Shamrock" by Mary Carolyn Davies and reprinted by permission of Rand McNally & Company.

UNIT FOUR

CHILDREN'S THEATER

PLAYMAKING
FOR EVERYONE
Floy Winks DeLancey

PLAYMAKING IS FUN

You have all seen moving picture and television plays. You all have your favorite actresses and actors.

Did you ever stop to think that *you* are an actor, too?

When you were small and pretended to be an airplane, you were acting. When you walked on hands and feet and barked like a dog, you were acting. Now when you play mother to your dolls, or when you play cowboy and Indian, or soldier, or airplane pilot, you are acting.

From this kind of acting, it is just a step to making a play. Some people get ideas for plays from stories they have read. Some people get ideas for plays from things that have happened in history. Sometimes things that happen to us every day make a good play.

197

THE FLYING SAUCER MYSTERY

Sometimes pictures tell a story that can be made into a play. On this page you will find a comic strip without any words. The characters are *doing* things, but they are not saying anything. You will have to decide for yourself what they are doing. You will have to decide what they might say while the action goes on.

Look at the comic strip carefully. Does it tell a story for you? What happens between the first picture and the last picture that would make a good play?

What do you think the characters in the comic strip are saying?

Act out the mystery in pantomime for the class. See if the *way you act* can tell the story without words.

PANTOMIMES TO GUESS

Actors have to learn to say many things without words. The way actors look and the way they act often tell how they feel. Here are some pantomime "pretends." Try to act one of the parts so the class can guess which character you are pretending to be. Be sure you know what each word below means before you begin acting.

FOR BOYS

1. a strong wrestler
2. a lazy boy mowing the lawn
3. a hardworking boy raking leaves
4. a young sailor on a rolling boat
5. an angry man whose window has been broken by a baseball

FOR GIRLS

1. a kind lady
2. a sulky girl
3. a frightened woman
4. a tired girl sweeping the porch
5. a nurse helping a sick person
6. a vain fashion model
7. a girl trying to put a worm on a fishhook

199

FOR TWO PUPILS

1. children walking barefoot in squashy mud
2. children walking barefoot on cinders
3. getting a haircut
4. playing marbles
5. helping Dad or Mother work at home
6. fishing with a small and noisy child

ACTING STORIES IN PANTOMIME

After you have read each story idea below, plan with your classmates how you would act out each one. Then present them for the class without any words.

1. Your horse has been stolen by a rustler. As you are looking for the horse, you come down a hill and find three of the rustlers around a fire.

2. You have broken something borrowed from your best friend. You have to tell your friend what has happened.

3. On a Cub Scout hike, you and two other boys have gone ahead of the leader. One boy falls and breaks his arm.

4. You have been sent to the store to buy three things. When you get there you can remember only two. The clerk suggests that you call your mother on the telephone to find out what the third thing is. You call her; then complete your order.

PLAYMAKING
WITH WORDS

Now that you have tried acting the stories on page 200 without words, add conversation to one of the stories and make a real play from it. Add words also to "The Flying Saucer Mystery" to make it into a real play.

PLAYS FROM
FAMOUS STORIES

On the next page is a Greek myth from olden days. You may want to make a play from this story. The play needs only one scene. You will find suggestions for playmaking at the end of the myth.

KING MIDAS

Long ago there lived a king named Midas. He was very greedy and thought of little but money and wealth. But he could also be very kind.

One day an old man named Silenus wandered into the house of Midas. Silenus had forgotten who he was and where he lived. Midas was good to the old man. He gave him food and took care of him.

Soon the son of Silenus came looking for him. The son's name was Bacchus. He had the power to grant wishes to people he liked.

"You have taken good care of my old father," Bacchus said to Midas. "As a reward, you may have any wish you desire."

Midas did not take time to think. He knew the very wish he wanted.

"I would like this wish," Midas said, "that everything I touch should turn into gold."

"That is a poor wish," Bacchus said. "But if that is what you want, that is the wish you shall have." So Bacchus gave Midas the power of the Golden Touch.

After Bacchus had left with his father, Midas sat down to think over his gift.

"I shall be the richest man in the whole world," he said to himself.

As he spoke he saw an ant crawling up his sleeve. He brushed it away. And there at his feet lay an ant made of solid gold. Midas looked down and saw that the chair in which he sat had turned to gold, too.

"This is wonderful, wonderful," he said.

He picked up an apple from the table by his side and started to take a bite. But the apple had already become a ball of gold.

"Beautiful," Midas said as he held up the golden apple.

But when dinner time came, Midas found that everything he touched to put to his lips turned to gold. He was very hungry, but he could have nothing to eat. Gold turnips, golden fish, and liquid gold instead of water stood on his table.

"I will starve! I will die!" moaned Midas. "Oh, why did I ever ask for such a foolish wish?"

Just at that moment Bacchus returned and looked in through the open door.

"Are you happy with your new gift?" he asked Midas.

Midas shook his head sadly.

"Bacchus! Bacchus!" he cried. "Please take my gift away from me. I have learned that there are more important things in the world than gold."

Bacchus smiled. "You have learned a good lesson, Midas," he said. "I can take away the gift if you wish. Go to the river Pactolus. Then bathe in its waters. The river will wash away your greediness."

Midas thanked Bacchus quickly. He could hardly wait to start for the river which would take away from him his selfish power.

PLANNING THE PLAY

1. Midas is alone on the stage counting his gold coins.

2. Silenus comes to the door. Midas brings him in and gives him food.

3. Bacchus comes looking for Silenus. He thanks Midas for caring for the old man and offers him a wish.

4. Midas wishes for the Golden Touch. Bacchus grants the wish unwillingly.

5. Bacchus and Silenus leave. Midas darts around the room touching things. He picks up an apple and starts to take a bite; then he turns his back to the audience and picks up an orange to be the golden apple.

6. He talks to himself about his wonderful new gift until the servant brings his dinner on a tray.

7. Midas discovers that he cannot eat or drink without turning food to gold.

8. Bacchus returns and takes away the Golden Touch. Midas prepares to leave for the river Pactolus.

THE STORY OF ECHO

Here is another story from long ago. As you read, think of how you could make it into a play.

In old Greek days, there lived a beautiful girl named Echo. She liked the woods and hills and wandered through them constantly, talking to herself. When she was with other people, she talked all the time, too. She talked so much that no one else had a chance to say anything at all.

Finally Echo's friends grew tired of listening to her all the time. One of her friends was a goddess with the power to cast spells. One day Echo and her friends sat by the side of a stream watching the blue sky and the trees bending in the winds. And, of course, Echo kept talking all the time about nothing at all.

"Do be quiet, Echo, and let us enjoy just looking at the beautiful world," begged the goddess.

But Echo kept talking on and on. She talked about herself and her friends and her new dresses and what she had to eat for dinner the night before.

Finally the goddess said to her, "Echo, from this time on you will never be able to say anything of your own. You will only be able to repeat the last few words of what your friends say."

And Echo soon found out that this was true. When she tried to speak, she could only repeat the words someone else had said.

To this very day, Echo lives in the caves and woods she used to love so well, repeating always what someone else has said.

PLANNING THE PLAY

1. Goddess and her friends are sitting together. They talk about Echo and how much Echo annoys them by talking all the time.

2. Echo enters. She starts talking about nothing at all.

3. Her friends ask her to be quiet. Echo keeps on talking.

4. The goddess pronounces the sentence that Echo will never be able to say anything of her own again.

5. Echo can only repeat the last words which any character on the stage says. As the other characters leave the stage, they say "good-by" to Echo. She echoes a weak "-by" as the curtain closes.

MAKING A PLAY WITH MORE THAN ONE SCENE

The Bible has many stories. Here is one that makes a good play. You are going to plan a play with different scenes. To help you, there are some suggestions on page 210, following the story.

NOAH AND THE ARK

Noah was a great and good man who lived in Bible times. One day the Lord spoke to Noah. He said, "The time has come when everyone on earth must die because they have been wicked. Only you and your family shall live. You, Noah, have tried to do what is right."

Noah asked how he and his family could live if all people on earth were to die.

"You must build a big ship, an ark," said the Lord. "Make the ship very long and very wide. It should look like a three-story house with a roof on top. Build it wide so it can float on the water."

Noah listened to what the Lord said. "I am going to bring a great flood," said the Lord. "All people and all animals will die in the flood. Therefore you must save some of the animals. The ark must be big enough to hold two of each kind of animal and bird on earth."

Noah and his three sons, whose names were Shem, Ham, and Japheth, worked hard and long to build the ark. At last it was finished. Soon the animals began coming — two of every kind in the world. There were elephants and tigers, cows and horses and sheep, doves and blackbirds, cats and dogs and parakeets.

Soon the rains came. Rain fell for forty days and forty nights until all the world was flooded.

But the ark rode on the water like a big ocean liner.

When the rain stopped, Noah wondered when it would be safe to leave the ark. First he sent out a black raven. When the raven did not return, Noah sent out a dove. The dove came back. The next day he sent the dove out again.

This time the dove carried a fresh green olive leaf in its mouth when it returned. Then Noah knew that the world was no longer flooded and that green things were growing once more. He knew it was time for all of them to leave the ark.

And just then a beautiful rainbow shone overhead. The rainbow was God's promise to Noah that all was well.

TWO PLANS FOR A NOAH'S ARK PLAY

Here are two plans for a play about Noah's Ark. Perhaps your class will be able to think of a third plan that you like better.

PLAN ONE: TWO SCENES

Characters. Noah and Mrs. Noah, Shem and Mrs. Shem, Ham and Mrs. Ham, Japheth and Mrs. Japheth, the Animals.

Scene 1. Noah and his sons are building the ark. As they hammer and pound, they talk about what God has told Noah. As they pound in the last nail on the big ship, their wives come in to report that the animals are coming, two by two.

You may choose to be whatever kind of animal or bird you like best. The animals enter the ark, and the first scene ends.

Scene 2. Noah and his family are talking about the forty days they have spent on the ark. They talk about how hard the rain has pounded and about how unhappy some of the animals have been.

One of the sons says the rain has stopped. Noah wonders how soon they can leave the ark. He sends the raven out to see what the world looks like.

Next he sends out the dove. The dove returns with an olive leaf in his mouth.

Noah and his family and all the animals are happy to know they can leave. As they open the doors of the ark, they see a rainbow in the sky. They know the rainbow is God's promise that all will be well with them.

PLAN TWO: THREE SCENES

Characters. The same as those in Plan One.

Scene 1. The forest. The animals are talking among themselves about the rumor that there is going to be a flood. The parrot tells what she has heard about Noah building an ark. The animals all wonder if they will have enough to eat on the ark.

Noah and one of his sons enter and ask the animals to come to the ark at once, as rain is already falling. They march off-stage in twos.

Scene 2. On the Ark. Noah and his family talk about the rain and God's promise that they will be saved.

The animals talk among themselves about the crowded quarters. The dog and the cat have a fight. The giraffe says he has a stiff neck from having to hold his head so low. No one wants to talk to the snakes.

Scene 3. On the Ark. The duck wants to go overboard for a swim. Noah says he must wait until they are certain there is dry land somewhere. He sends out the raven and the dove together to find land.

The dove returns with the olive leaf. The animals are happy and each one laughs happily in his own way: the donkey brays, the lion roars, the dog barks, etc. Noah opens the doors of the ark, and there is a great rush to go outside. A rainbow can be seen when the doors are opened.

A THEATER PLAY

RUMPELSTILTSKIN

Dramatization by Floy Winks DeLancey

CHARACTERS

King

Maysel

George, *Maysel's father*

Rumpelstiltskin

Rodney, *a workman*

Prince Johann, *the
King's brother*

Several lords and
ladies (Francis,
Lenore, Lucy, Robert, etc.)

SCENE 1. *Room in King's palace. King is on throne. Several men are talking with him.*

KING. These are marvelous things you have been telling me about your daughters, gentlemen. Perhaps one of them will prove fit to marry my young brother. He will be king one day, and must soon choose a bride. What was it you said your daughter could do, Francis?

FRANCIS. She can cook the most wonderful spaghetti in the world, your Highness. It is a dream. (*He rubs his stomach and licks his lips.*)

KING. Very good, very good. But one would tire of spaghetti night after night. And your daughter, Robert? What was it you said she could do?

ROBERT. My daughter, your Highness, my daughter can sing more sweetly than the nightingale. Such music as comes from her red lips! (*He hums a tune.*)

KING. Humph! Music is all right. But you can't eat music, or spend it, either. And you, George, you have said nothing so far. What is it your daughter Maysel can do?

GEORGE. Your Highness, my daughter Maysel has a wonderful gift. Your Highness, she can spin straw — common, everyday straw out of the barnyard — into gold. Right into gold she spins it, sire.

214

KING. What a marvelous gift this! Bring her here. If what you say is true, she shall marry my brother. Fancy having a sister-in-law who can turn straw into gold! Fetch her here at once!

GEORGE. But your Highness — (*He looks frightened.*)

KING. Fetch her, I say. (*George leaves.*) And you, men, you may leave, too. I want no one around when I talk with this Maysel. Gold! Straw into gold! Wonderful!

(*The men leave, muttering among themselves: "My daughter is more beautiful." "My daughter's spaghetti is better than gold," etc. Enter George, leading Maysel by the hand. She tries to pull back and looks frightened.*)

KING. Enter, my dear. Enter. Your father has been telling me wonderful things about you.

MAYSEL. But I can't, your Majesty, I —

KING. There now! A modest maiden, too. She

215

does not brag. But your father has told me.

GEORGE. But your Majesty —

KING. Not another word. We will leave your daughter here now, George. My men shall bring straw and a spinning wheel. In the morning I shall expect to find a nice lot of gold in the room, Maysel.

MAYSEL (*crying*). But your Majesty —

KING (*angrily*). Not another word! I want the straw spun into gold. Then you shall marry my brother. But if you fail —

GEORGE. What, your Majesty? If she fails —

KING. If there is no spun gold in this room in the morning, Maysel shall die. Come, George. (*King leaves; Maysel takes hold of her father's arm.*)

MAYSEL. What shall I do, Father? What shall I do?

GEORGE. I'll think of something, Daughter. I never dreamed he would ask for proof.

KING (*outside*). George, come!
(*As George hurries out, King's men enter bringing straw and a spinning wheel. They place them on the floor and leave. Maysel sits on the floor with her head in her arms and cries.*)

MAYSEL. What shall I do? No one can spin straw into gold. No one!
(*Enter Rumpelstiltskin.*)

216

RUMPEL. You are wrong, Maysel. There is someone who can spin straw into gold. I can!

MAYSEL (*jumping to her feet*). You can? Oh, please, little man, whoever you are, please spin the straw for me. I die tomorrow if you will not help me.

RUMPEL. And what will you give me if I do this for you?

MAYSEL. Anything, anything, little man, whatever your name is.

RUMPEL. Never mind about my name. Will you give me your first-born son if I do this for you?

MAYSEL. Anything, anything.

RUMPEL. Very well, then. Sit down and close your eyes. Keep quiet. I do not like girls who chatter and talk. Be quiet, and when you open your eyes, the straw will have turned into gold.

(*Maysel sits down and closes her eyes. Rumpelstiltskin sits down at the spinning wheel and picks up some straw. As he turns the wheel, he picks up spun gold — which is*

217

really a hank of golden colored yarn! — from the other side of the wheel.)

RUMPEL. Now, Maysel. Open your eyes. Here is your gold. But remember, your first-born son is mine. (*He leaves.*)

(*Maysel examines the gold. The King enters.*)

KING. Gold! Gold! I never believed it could be true. (*Enter his followers and the Prince. King turns to Prince.*) See the gold, brother Johann? This wonderful girl shall be your wife.

PRINCE. A beautiful girl she is, King. A beautiful girl.

(*King takes Maysel's hand and puts it into the Prince's hand. Curtain falls.*)

SCENE 2. *Two years later. Room in the castle. Maysel and the Prince are sitting together with a baby between them.*

PRINCE. Isn't he the most beautiful child you ever saw, Maysel?

MAYSEL. He is lovely! Prince Marcus, my little son! And he will grow to be a king.

(*Prince rises and walks to door.*)

218

PRINCE. I go to see my brother now, Maysel. But I will be back soon. You and the Prince and I must go for a walk in the bright autumn sun. (*He leaves.*)
(*Maysel starts singing a lullaby to the baby. Rumpelstiltskin enters.*)

RUMPEL. Aha! So you have your first-born son, Maysel. I will take him now.

MAYSEL (*jumping up in fright*). Who are you? Go away!

RUMPEL. Have you forgotten so soon? Who spun the straw into gold?

MAYSEL (*remembering*). Oh — oh — I never thought — You can't hold me to my promise!

RUMPEL. Oh, yes I can.

MAYSEL. Please, please — you cannot take my baby. (*She backs away from him.*)

RUMPEL. (*laughing*). Oh, yes I can. But you may have one chance. If you tell me what my name is, you may keep the child. I'll be back. (*He leaves.*)

MAYSEL. Little man, little man — (*Running

after him; then she stops and calls.) Johann, Rodney, Lenore, Lucy, come, come!
(*Prince and other characters come running in at her call.*)

MAYSEL. Quick, help me find out the name of the little man who just left. See, (*She points out the window.*) there he goes now. I must know his name or he will take the baby. Oh, Johann!

PRINCE. Take the baby! What do you mean?

MAYSEL. I promised him so long ago I had forgotten all about it. He spun the straw into gold for me, and I promised he could have my first son. Now if I cannot find out his name he will take the baby.
(*She begins to cry.*)

PRINCE. Rodney, Lenore, Lucy — go quickly. Tell all my men to ask anyone they see what the name of the little man is. Quick! Run!
(*All hurry out. Johann tries to comfort Maysel. Lenore puts her head through the door.*)

LENORE. Could his name be Humperdoodle?
(*Lucy sticks her head through door on other side of the stage.*)

LUCY. Could his name be Mulligan Stew?
(*Each character in turn calls in some suggestion. Finally Rodney comes into the room.*)

RODNEY. Your Highness, I have found no one who knows the name of the little man but —

MAYSEL. Yes, yes — quick, what have you found out?

RODNEY. As I hunted through the wood to find someone to ask, I saw a funny little man hop out of the bushes. About so high, he was. And he wore a red coat.

MAYSEL. Yes, yes, that sounds like my little man. Quick, what do you know?

RODNEY. The little man was hopping up and down and around and around like this.
(*Rodney hops up and down and around and around.*)

MAYSEL. Yes, hurry. What do you know?

RODNEY. And as he hopped he sang this little song:

> Today I bake, tomorrow I brew,
> The day after that Maysel's son is mine;
> And oh! I am glad that nobody knew
> That the name I am called is
>   Rumpelstiltskin!

221

MAYSEL. Oh, Rodney, how can I thank you? Now I can save my baby.

(*Rodney leaves. As he goes out one door Rumpelstiltskin enters from the other.*)

RUMPEL. (*rubbing his hands together*). And have you found out my name yet, Princess?

MAYSEL (*thinking hard*). Could it be Mulligan?

RUMPEL. (*laughs loudly*). Mulligan! Ha! Ha! Try again.

(*Maysel pretends to cry.*)

MAYSEL. Could it be Humperdoodle? Or Montmorency Gustavus Archibald?

RUMPEL. (*laughs harder*). One more guess and the baby is mine.

MAYSEL. Could your name be — could your name be — RUMPELSTILTSKIN?

RUMPEL. (*jumping up and down and screaming in anger*). How did you know? How did you know?

(*While he is hopping up and down the Prince and his followers enter. Scene ends with Prince and Princess holding baby between them while Lords and Ladies dance around. Rumpelstiltskin crawls out the door and is never seen again.*)

CURTAIN

PANTOMIME WITH POEMS

Here are some short poems about the out-of-doors. How would you pretend to be the wind, the sun, the moon? As you read the poems, watch for the words that tell *how* something moves. How would you pantomime the word *creep?* *solemn?* *cuddle?* *pulling?* *rolls?*

WHO HAS SEEN THE WIND?

Christina Rossetti

Who has seen the wind?
  Neither I nor you.
But when the leaves hang trembling,
  The wind is passing through.

Who has seen the wind?
  Neither you nor I;
But when the trees bow down their heads,
  The wind is passing by.

223

MOON–COME–OUT

Eleanor Farjeon

Moon-Come-Out
And Sun-Go-In,
Here's a soft blanket
To cuddle your chin.

Moon-Go-In
And Sun-Come-Out,
Throw off the blanket
And bustle about.

CLOUDS

Christina Rossetti

White sheep, white sheep, on a blue hill,
When the wind stops, you all stand still.
When the wind blows, you walk away slow.
White sheep, white sheep, where do you go?

FOG

Carl Sandburg

The fog comes
on little cat feet.

It sits looking
over harbor and city
on silent haunches
and then moves on.

ACTING POEMS
IN COSTUME

These poems need both acting and costumes. Some children may want to say or read the poems while others act them out. The first poem can end with a march around the room.

For the next poem, what could you use for the donkey's costume? When you choose children to take the parts, you may want to choose three kind ladies. Each lady may act out one stanza of the poem.

MARCHING SONG

Robert Louis Stevenson

Bring the comb and play upon it!
   Marching, here we come!
Willie cocks his highland bonnet,
   Johnnie beats the drum.

Mary Jane commands the party,
   Peter leads the rear;
Feet in time, alert and hearty,
   Each a Grenadier!

226

All in the most martial manner
  Marching double-quick;
While the napkin, like a banner,
  Waves upon the stick!

Here's enough for fame and pillage,
  Great commander Jane!
Now that we've been round the village,
  Let's go home again.

MY DONKEY

Rose Fyleman

My donkey, my dear,
Had a pain in his head;
A kind lady gave him
A bonnet of red,
And little shoes of lavender,
Lav — lav — lavender,
And little shoes of lavender
To keep him from the cold.

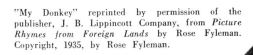

"My Donkey" reprinted by permission of the
publisher, J. B. Lippincott Company, from *Picture
Rhymes from Foreign Lands* by Rose Fyleman.
Copyright, 1935, by Rose Fyleman.

227

My donkey, my dear,
Had a pain in his throat;
A kind lady gave him
A button-up coat,
And little shoes of lavender,
Lav — lav — lavender,
And little shoes of lavender
To keep him from the cold.

My donkey, my dear,
Had a pain in his chest;
A kind lady gave him
A thick woolly vest,
And little shoes of lavender,
Lav — lav — lavender,
And little shoes of lavender
To keep him from the cold.

A POEM TO CHANT

Here is a good poem to say aloud. In the
first stanza, try to make your chanting sound like
the clop-clop of a horse's hoofs.

HORSESHOE

Edna St. Vincent Millay

Wonder where this horseshoe went.
Up and down, up and down,
Up and past the monument,
Maybe into town.

Wait a minute. "Horseshoe,
How far have you been?"
Says it's been to Salem
And halfway to Lynn.

Wonder who was in the team.
Wonder what they saw.
Wonder if they passed a bridge —
Bridge with a draw.

Says it went from one bridge
Straight upon another.
Says it took a little girl
Driving with her mother.

"Horseshoe" Section VII of "From a Very Little Sphinx" in *Poems Selected for Young People*, published by Harper & Brothers. Copyright, 1923, 1951, by Edna St. Vincent Millay.

A FOLK SONG AND DANCE

This American folk song has been sung in our country for many years. It is a good song for square dancing.

SOURWOOD MOUNTAIN

Chick - en a crow - in' on Sour - wood
Moun - tain, Hey! day de ling dum a day!
Whis - tle up your dogs and we'll all go
hunt - ing Hey! day de ling dum a day!

My true love loves dogs and gunnin', Hey! day, etc.
But when I call him, he comes runnin'!, Hey! day, etc.
My true love's a blue-eyed daisy, Hey! day, etc.
She won't work and I'm too lazy! Hey! day, etc.
Night comin' down on Sourwood Mountain, Hey! day, etc.
So many bright stars I can't count 'em! Hey! day, etc.

UNIT FIVE

OUR LAND
LONG AGO

STAYING
ALONE

Laura Ingalls Wilder

Summer was gone, winter was coming, and now it was time for Pa to make a trip to town. Here in Minnesota, town was so near that Pa would be gone only one day, and Ma was going with him.

She took Carrie, because Carrie was too little to be left far from Ma. But Mary and Laura were big girls. Mary was going on nine and Laura was going on eight, and they could stay home and take care of everything while Pa and Ma were gone.

For going-to-town, Ma made a new dress for Carrie, from the pink calico that Laura had worn when she was little. There was enough of it to make Carrie a little pink sunbonnet. Carrie's hair had been in curl-papers all night. It hung in long, golden, round curls, and when Ma tied the pink sunbonnet strings under Carrie's chin, Carrie looked like a rose.

"Staying Alone" from *On the Banks of Plum Creek* by Laura Ingalls Wilder. Copyright, 1937, Harper & Brothers.

Ma wore her hoopskirts and her best dress, the beautiful challis with little strawberries on it, that she had worn to the sugar-dancing at Grandma's long ago in the Big Woods.

"Now be good girls, Laura and Mary," was the last thing she said. She was on the wagon seat, with Carrie beside her. Their lunch was in the wagon. Pa took up the ox goad.

"We'll be back before sundown," he promised. "Hi-oop!" he said to Pete and Bright. The big ox and the little one leaned into their yoke and the wagon started.

"Good-by, Pa! Good-by, Ma! Good-by, Carrie, good-by!" Laura and Mary called after it.

Slowly the wagon went away. Pa walked beside the oxen. Ma and Carrie, the wagon, and Pa all grew smaller, till they were gone into the prairie.

The prairie seemed big and empty then, but there was nothing to be afraid of. There were no wolves and no Indians. Besides, Jack stayed close to Laura. Jack was a responsible dog. He

knew that he must take care of everything when Pa was away.

That morning Mary and Laura played by the creek, among the rushes. They did not go near the swimming hole. They did not touch the straw stack. At noon they ate the corn dodgers and molasses and drank the milk that Ma had left for them. They washed their tin cups and put them away.

Then Laura wanted to play on the big rock, but Mary wanted to stay in the dugout. She said that Laura must stay there, too.

"Ma can make me," Laura said, "but you can't."

"I can so," said Mary. "When Ma's not here, you have to do what I say because I'm older."

"You have to let me have my way because I'm littler," said Laura.

"That's Carrie, it isn't you," Mary told her. "If you don't do what I say, I'll tell Ma."

"I guess I can play where I want to!" said Laura.

Mary grabbed at her, but Laura was too quick.

235

She darted out, and she would have run up the path, but Jack was in the way. He stood stiff, looking across the creek. Laura looked too, and she screeched, "Mary!"

The cattle were all around Pa's haystacks. They were eating the hay. They were tearing into the stacks with their horns, gouging out hay, eating it and trampling over it.

There would be nothing left to feed Pete and Bright and Spot in the wintertime.

Jack knew what to do. He ran growling down the steps to the footbridge. Pa was not there to save the haystacks; they must drive those cattle away.

"Oh, we can't! We can't!" Mary said, scared. But Laura ran behind Jack, and Mary came after her. They went over the creek and past the spring. They came up on the prairie, and now they saw the fierce, big cattle quite near. The long horns were gouging, the thick legs trampling and jostling, the wide mouths bawling.

Mary was too scared to move. Laura was too scared to stand still. She jerked Mary along. She saw a stick, and grabbed it up and ran yelling at the cattle. Jack ran at them, growling. A big red cow swiped at him with her horns, but he jumped behind her. She snorted and galloped. All the other cattle ran humping and jostling after her, and Jack and Laura and Mary ran after them.

But they could not chase those cattle away from the haystacks. The cattle ran around and around and in between the stacks, jostling and bawling, tearing off hay and trampling it. More and more hay slid off the stacks. Laura ran panting and yelling, waving her stick. The faster she ran, the faster the cattle went, black and brown and red, brindle and spotted cattle, big and with awful horns, and they would not stop wasting the hay. Some tried to climb over the toppling stacks.

Laura was hot and dizzy. Her hair unbraided

237

and blew in her eyes. Her throat was rough
from yelling, but she kept on yelling, running,
and waving her stick. She was too scared to hit
one of those big, horned cows. More and more
hay kept coming down, faster and faster they
trampled over it.

Suddenly Laura turned around and ran the
other way. She faced the big red cow coming
around a haystack.

The huge legs and shoulders and terrible horns
were coming fast. Laura could not scream now.
But she jumped at that cow and waved her
stick. The cow tried to stop, but all the other
cattle were coming behind her and she couldn't.
She swerved and ran away across the ploughed
ground, all the others galloping after her.

Jack and Laura and Mary chased them, farther
and farther from the hay. Far into the high
prairie grasses they chased those cattle. . . .

They went back through the high grass that
dragged at their trembling legs. They were glad
to drink at the spring. They were glad to be in
the quiet dugout and sit down to rest.

All that long, quiet afternoon they stayed in
the dugout. The cattle did not come back to
the haystacks. Slowly the sun went down the
western sky. Soon it would be time to meet the
cattle at the big gray rock, and Laura and Mary
wished that Pa and Ma would come home.

Again and again they went up the path to look for the wagon. At last they sat waiting with Jack on the grassy top of their house. The lower the sun went, the more attentive Jack's ears were. Often he and Laura stood up to look at the edge of the sky where the wagon had gone, though they could see it just as well when they were sitting down.

Finally Jack turned one ear that way, then the other. Then he looked up at Laura and a waggle went from his neck to his stubby tail. The wagon was coming!

They all stood and watched till it came out of the prairie. When Laura saw the oxen, and Ma and Carrie on the wagon seat, she jumped up and down, swinging her sunbonnet and shouting, "They're coming! They're coming!"

"They're coming awful fast," Mary said.

Laura was still. She heard the wagon rattling loudly. Pete and Bright were coming fast. They were running. They were running away.

The wagon came bumpity-banging and bounc-

ing. Laura saw Ma down in a corner of the
wagon box, hanging onto it and hugging Carrie.
Pa came bounding in long jumps beside Bright,
shouting and hitting at Bright with the goad.

He was trying to turn Bright back from the
creek bank.

He could not do it. The big oxen galloped
nearer and nearer the steep edge. Bright was
pushing Pa off it. They were all going over.
The wagon, Ma, and Carrie were going to fall
down the bank, all the way down to the creek.

Pa shouted a terrible shout. He struck Bright's
head with all his might, and Bright swerved.
Laura ran screaming. Jack jumped at Bright's
nose. Then the wagon, Ma, and Carrie flashed
by. Bright crashed against the stable, and suddenly everything was still.

Pa ran after the wagon and Laura ran behind
him.

"Whoa, Bright! Whoa, Pete," Pa said. He

held onto the wagon box and looked at Ma.

"We're all right, Charles," Ma said. Her face was gray and she was shaking all over.

Pete was trying to go on through the doorway into the stable, but he was yoked to Bright and Bright was headed against the stable wall. Pa lifted Ma and Carrie out of the wagon, and Ma said, "Don't cry, Carrie. See, we're all right."

Carrie's pink dress was torn down the front. She snuffled against Ma's neck and tried to stop crying as Ma told her.

"Oh, Caroline! I thought you were going over the bank," Pa said.

"I thought so, too, for a minute," Ma answered. "But I might have known you wouldn't let that happen."

"Pshaw!" said Pa. "It was good old Pete. He wasn't running away. Bright was, but Pete was only going along. He saw the stable and wanted his supper."

But Laura knew that Ma and Carrie would have fallen down into the creek with the wagon and oxen, if Pa had not run so fast and hit Bright so hard. She crowded against Ma's hoop-skirt and hugged her tight and said, "Oh, Ma! Oh, Ma!" So did Mary.

"There, there," said Ma. "All's well that ends well. Now, girls, help bring in the packages while Pa puts up the oxen."

They carried all the little packages into the

241

dugout. They met the cattle at the gray rock and put Spot into the stable, and Laura helped milk her while Mary helped Ma get supper.

At supper, they told how the cattle had got into the haystacks and how they had driven them away. Pa said they had done exactly the right thing. He said, "We knew we could depend on you to take care of everything. Didn't we, Caroline?"

They had completely forgotten that Pa always brought them presents from town, until after supper he pushed back his bench and looked as if he expected something. Then Laura jumped on his knee, and Mary sat on the other, and Laura bounced and asked, "What did you bring us, Pa? What? What?"

"Guess," Pa said.

They could not guess. But Laura felt something crackle in his jumper pocket, and she pounced on it. She pulled out a paper bag, beautifully striped with tiny red and green stripes. And in the bag were two sticks of candy, one for Mary and one for Laura!

They were maple-sugar-colored, and they were flat on one side.

Mary licked hers. But Laura bit her stick, and the outside of it came off, crumbly. The inside was hard and clear and dark brown. And it had a rich, brown, tangy taste. Pa said it was hoarhound candy.

After the dishes were done, Laura and Mary each took her stick of candy and they sat on Pa's

knees, outside the door in the cool dusk. Ma sat just inside the dugout, humming to Carrie in her arms.

The creek was talking to itself under the yellow willows. One by one the great stars swung low and seemed to quiver and flicker in the little wind.

Laura was snug in Pa's arm. His beard softly tickled her cheek, and the delicious candy-taste melted on her tongue.

After a while she said, "Pa."

"What, little half-pint?" Pa's voice asked against her hair.

"I think I like wolves better than cattle," she said.

"Cattle are more useful, Laura," Pa said.

She thought about that a while. Then she said, "Anyway, I like wolves better."

She was not contradicting; she was only saying what she thought.

"Well, Laura, we're going to have a good team of horses before long," Pa said. She knew when that would be. It would be when they had a wheat crop.

WHAT HAPPENED?

The cattle must be stopped. They were tearing down the haystacks. Nothing would be left for winter. Laura finally chased the cattle away. How did she do it?

244

Laura and Mary looked and looked for Ma and Pa to return. They could see nothing. At last even though the girls still could not see the wagon, they knew Ma and Pa were coming. How did the girls know?

Once the wagon came into view, Laura and Mary could see it was going very fast. Soon it was clear the oxen were running away. Pa couldn't stop them. Yet if he didn't, the wagon would go over the bank. And Ma and Carrie would fall with it. What did Pa do?

THINK IT OVER

Pa brought Laura and Mary something. What was it? After supper, Laura and Mary sat with Pa outside the door. How do you think they felt? What makes you think so?

In the pioneer days of this story, boys and girls were on their own earlier than they are now. They had real jobs on the farm even before they were as old as you are now. Often they had to look out for themselves as did Laura and Mary.

Nowadays it's harder to feel that you are on your own. But you can make a start. You can take care of your own room. You can do little jobs for your neighbors. When you do some of these things on your own you show that you are growing up. What else can you do to show that you are growing up?

245

OLD LOG HOUSE

James S. Tippett

On a little green knoll
At the edge of the wood
My great-great-grandmother's
First house stood.

The house was of logs,
My grandmother said,
With one big room
And a lean-to shed.

The logs were cut
And the house was raised
By pioneer men
In the olden days.

I like to hear
My grandmother tell
How they built the fireplace
And dug the well.

They split the shingles;
They filled each chink;
It's a house of which
I like to think.

Forever and ever
I wish I could
Live in a house
At the edge of a wood.

"Old Log House" from *A World to Know* by James S.
Tippett. Copyright, 1933, Harper & Brothers.

THAT NOISY BOY

Margaret Macy Ballard

Peter Folger was having a wonderful time
looking out to sea from the top of his grandmother's windmill. He was having such fun
because he was pretending he was on a Nantucket
whaleship sighting a whale. And that was an
exciting game for a boy to play about a hundred
years ago on Nantucket Island. Especially when
that boy's father was a whaling captain miles
away at sea.

Besides, the whale that Peter was pretending
to see aloft from his grandmother's windmill was
a silver whale with a white stomach. He was
King of the Pacific. So when Peter yelled at the
top of his voice, "Blo-o-ows, she blows. Blo-o-ows,
there she blows," it came out just about the

loudest noise a ten-year-old boy had ever made anywhere. For no matter what Peter said or how quietly he tried to speak, the result was LOUD.

He tried again, even louder, the call the sailor up in the lookout always made when he saw a whale.

"Blo-o-ows. She blows. Blo-o-ows."

He waited, almost hoping a real officer of the deck would call up to him. "Where-away?"

And then Peter could answer where he saw the King Whale. "Two points off the starboard bow."

But when he looked down from the windmill, the silver whale was only his grandmother's gray house with white trimmings. As for the officer of the deck, it wasn't the second mate in neat blue uniform but his grandmother in plain Quaker dress.

"Get thee down from there, Peter Folger," she called as she came near. "Never have I heard such a noise. All the whales in the ocean will be sounding after that."

Peter was down in a hurry and standing before his grandmother.

"Thee's a big, lazy boy," she went on. "Always sighting whales. Time enough for that when thee

goes to sea with thy father. Meanwhile there is the woodpile. And the Widow Coffin's plate I told thee to take back early this morning. Now get along, Peter, and try to remember thy dignity and keep thy voice down as becomes a Friend and not a hoodlum. Thee makes twice the noise the Town Crier does."

"Yes, Grandmother," Peter replied, politely. The words must have come out louder than he intended, for Grandmother threw her hands over her ears and hurried into the house, saying, "That noisy boy!"

Peter was glad his grandmother had mentioned the Town Crier. He decided to see if he could find the Crier and go his rounds with him, at the same time stopping to leave Widow Coffin's plate. For Peter loved to walk and talk with Mr. Macy, the Town Crier, even more than he liked to sight imaginary whales. Sometimes the Crier would let Peter ring his brass bell to get people's attention. Then Mr. Macy would cry out the news or the advertising for the storekeepers. Peter also liked to see the summer visitors from the mainland.

As Peter turned into Main Street he saw Mr. Macy coming out of his house. He knew it was nine o'clock because Mr. Macy made his morning cries at that time. Peter caught up with him.

"Thought thee was catching whales," Mr. Macy said. He chuckled. "I'll make thee a crier yet. Some folks have a talent for one thing, some for another.

"Come along. The wind's shifted so the boat from New Bedford will be late. No news yet. Mr. Clark's got fresh beans to sell. Meat auction tomorrow. I've got a cold and don't feel much like making rhymes, but I presume likely I'll make one or two just to please folks."

Peter grinned. Lots of times Mr. Macy announced all the news in rhyme. He always made at least one jingle.

Halfway up the block, he gave Peter the bell to ring and as soon as Peter had done a good job

251

of ringing, Mr. Macy threw back his head and bellowed:

Nine o'clock and all is well.
Stop your talking and hear me tell.
If you're wanting news, you'll have to wait.
Boat from New Bedford's coming in late.
Tomorrow at ten come down the street
To the lower square to get your meat:
Beef and pork, mutton and lamb.
Also auctioning off some ham.

Up and down the street went Peter and the Town Crier until all the news and advertisements were cried several times over. Then Peter left his package at the Widow Coffin's and walked back home with Mr. Macy.

"Folks mostly want to know about the boat," said Mr. Macy. "Seems as if they're either wanting to get on the Island or off again. Or they want the mail. Sure have to let folks know."

Mr. Macy turned in his own gate. "Now get along, Peter, and help thy grandmother. I won't cry again until this evening and then not much. Got a cold and getting hoarse."

Peter ran up the street. He suddenly remembered the woodpile. Besides, he was very hungry.

He might have slipped down to the village again that evening, but his grandmother kept him busy at one thing and another until it was dark and time for bed. But Peter heard Mr. Macy announce that the boat would leave sharp at eight o'clock in the morning.

Now Peter liked nothing better than to be on hand when the boat was getting ready to sail. So he got up with the sun, ate a cold biscuit, drank some milk, and was off to the harbor.

Down at the wharf, Peter discovered a lot more activity than was usual so early in the morning, and he wondered if it were later than he thought. Mail and packages were being loaded, and Captain Gardner was busy giving orders. Peter went right up to him, though, because he liked nothing better than to help and maybe earn a penny or two besides.

"Any work, sir?" he asked.

The Captain jumped. "Thee needn't yell so loud, Peter Folger. Aye, there's work to be done. We're getting under way in thirty minutes.

Wind's changed, barometer's falling. I sent word to Crier Macy twenty minutes ago to warn folks, and not a sound from him yet. Thee run down to his house, Peter, and tell him."

Mr. Macy shook his head sadly when he saw Peter. He looked very unhappy.

"Yes, I know about the boat's sailing an hour earlier," he whispered to Peter. "Can't do a thing about it. Voice is gone."

Peter looked startled. "Gone?" He whispered, too, thinking maybe someone was still in bed.

"First I ever heard thee speak below a shout," smiled the Crier. "It's this confounded cold. Lost my voice."

Peter nodded sympathetically. He couldn't think of anything worse. "I'll go back and tell Cap'n Gardner." He shouted without meaning to.

"No, no," cried Mr. Macy hoarsely. "Anyone with a voice like that can do it himself. Get the bell from my table and get along and cry the news for me."

Peter pointed to himself in surprise.

"Don't stand there. Get the bell and go. I'll be listening for what thee has to tell folks about the sailing."

Peter stood in front of Mr. Macy's house for a few minutes, the brass bell in one hand, his chin in the other. Then suddenly he gave a leap in the air and began to ring the bell as he started up the street.

Like Mr. Macy, he threw back his head and opened his mouth. And there came out a cry loud enough to wake Nantucket Island from end to end.

> Wake up, folks, and don't be slow.
> Seven o'clock and the boat will go.
> The wind is up and the barometer's down.
> She's sailing at seven for New Bedford Town.
> It's Peter Folger crying so bold
> 'Cause Mr. Macy's home with a cold.

255

So Peter cried up and down the village streets until the whole town was awake and stirring.

He finally reached his own house near the edge of the town. Even as he turned the corner, he could see his grandmother in the doorway. She didn't look exactly angry. She looked more as if she couldn't believe what she saw and heard.

So Peter stopped right at the gate and shouted with a mighty shout:

> Grandmother, Grandmother,
> Come and hear
> Thy grandson, Peter, loud and clear.
> He's not so much at chopping wood
> But when he cries, his crying's good.

When Peter looked at his grandmother again she was shaking her head, but there was a broad smile on her face.

WHAT HAPPENED?

Peter Folger had a big voice. Grandmother thought it was too big. When she heard him pretending to see whales, she decided to give him something else to do. What did Grandmother give Peter to do?

On his way to carry out one of Grandmother's orders, Peter saw the Town Crier. Peter walked along with him. The Town Crier not only told the news but where to buy things. What sale was the Town Crier telling about?

Peter was up early the next morning to watch the boat getting ready to sail. Usually Mr. Macy, the Town Crier, would be warning people to get on board if they expected to sail. But not a sound came from Mr. Macy. What was wrong?

Peter became Town Crier for the day. He shouted a special jingle for Grandmother. How did she like it?

THINK IT OVER

"Some folks have a talent for one thing, some for another," said the Town Crier. That's a good thing to remember. Some boys are good in sports. Some girls are good in plays. Some boys draw good pictures. Some girls write good stories. Some boys and girls are good at getting along with people. Sometimes you think a boy or a girl can't do anything well. But that is never true.

If you think long enough, you'll see that every boy and girl in your class has something he does well. Suppose you were a talent scout. What talents would you find in your class?

257

THEN

Walter de la Mare

Twenty, forty, sixty, eighty,
  A hundred years ago,
All through the night with lantern bright
  The Watch trudged to and fro.
And little boys tucked snug abed
  Would wake from dreams to hear —
"Two o' the morning by the clock,
  And the stars a-shining clear!"
Or, when across the chimney-tops
  Screamed shrill a Northeast gale,
A faint and shaken voice would shout,
  "Three! and a storm of hail!"

JOHNNY AND THE INDIANS

Elizabeth Coatsworth

Johnny was a real boy who lived a long time ago in Plymouth. This was one of the first settlements of white people in our country. Johnny knew he must never go into the woods alone for fear he would get lost. Then too, there were unfriendly Indians in the woods. These Indians were not like Squanto, who dressed and talked like the English.

One day the dog Trojan ran into the wood and Johnny followed him. Soon both the boy and the dog were lost and could not find their way home.

For several days they wandered. They ate berries and strange fruits and drank water from

259

the streams.   Then they came to an Indian
camp.   At first Johnny was frightened, but the
sachem, or chief, told the Indians to be kind to
him.   They gave him food and a place to sleep,
with Trojan by his side.

All day the Indians talked and talked about the
lost child.   When Johnny woke up in the late
afternoon and the woman gave him more food,
they were still talking.

Some pointed one way, and some another.
They were very earnest.   Probably some wanted
to take him back to Plymouth, and some didn't.
Some perhaps thought that if Captain Standish
should come to the village with his musket, he
would accuse them of stealing Johnny, and maybe
make his musket go bang-bang among them.

The sachem must have decided that it would
be safer to take Johnny further away, for on the
second morning, when he and Trojan were rested
and well fed again, the Indians led him down to

the shore where a canoe was waiting with two
men to paddle it. Johnny and Trojan were told
to get into it. The young Indian woman looked
very sad. She gave Johnny a soft deerskin, with
colored ornaments on it, and a necklace of shells,
and one of the children gave him a fish made out
of clay. The whole village came to see him off,
and the women sang him a song which must have
meant "Good-by," and everyone pushed off the
canoe and shouted as the paddles began to dip
into the bright sea water.

Johnny waved and shouted, and Trojan barked
excitedly. This was wonderful! Johnny was no
longer hungry and he did not need to walk. He
had always wanted to go out on the bay, at
Plymouth, but no one would ever take him. Only
the men could go in the shallop to explore, or
trade with the Indians. They couldn't be bothered

with little boys. But now Johnny had a boat
all to himself, and Trojan for company, and two
Indians to do the work.

He thought he was going to Plymouth, but he
really didn't care very much. He was having too
much fun. The sun was warm and there were
lots of sea gulls flying about. The sea was bright
and almost still. He could look deep down into
the water. Sometimes he could see fish swimming
past. Once a wet dark head appeared nearby,
and a seal stared at them. Trojan barked at the
seal, and the seal barked back and then disappeared from sight.

On their right there were sand dunes. The
Indians paddled for a long time, and then they
all went ashore and ate something which they
had brought with them. And they drank from a
spring which the men knew about.

That evening they slept in a village they called
Cummaquid, where there was a young sachem,
and everyone was kind. Once more Johnny and
Trojan felt very important. The Indians wanted
to touch them and look at them, as though they

262

were something wonderful. No one in Plymouth thought Johnny or Trojan wonderful. In fact Johnny, with his shouts and tousled hair, got more frowns than smiles there. But in the Indian villages it was different. If he made a face showing the hole where his teeth were out, the children laughed and giggled. If he pointed to his mouth, the women hurried to bring him food. If he spoke, the men tried to understand him. They all talked about him for hours.

It was quite a change for Johnny.

Next day the people of Cummaquid came down to the shore to see him off. There was a wind today, and it was a little cold sitting still in the bottom of the canoe, and sometimes they were all wet with spray. But it was fun to bounce up and down among the waves, and once they saw three porpoises playing follow-the-leader a little distance away, leaping in and out of the water, black and shiny.

Late that evening they came to a bend in the shore, with long low flats good for clamming, and beyond the flats there were small pine trees and a pond with a village beside it. The village was called Nauset, and the sachem was called Aspinet.

Trojan and Johnny liked Nauset. They slept in another basket-shaped house and played games with the Indian children. The Indian women took off Johnny's torn clothes and tied his deerskin cloak about his shoulders. When their dogs wanted to fight with Trojan, they yelled and threw stones at them until they learned to let the English dog alone. Johnny went hunting with the men and berry-picking with the women and played games with the children. And wherever Johnny went, Trojan went, too.

"Does Mother ever cry for me?" Johnny asked of Trojan, as they walked along the shore. But Trojan only barked and swam out into the water after a stick. He was never homesick for a minute. Johnny was. For the time being this was fun. He liked it. But these weren't his people. This village wasn't his village. He wanted to tell his father of his adventures. And have his mother lean over the bed to kiss him good night. But he supposed he'd never see any of them again.

When Johnny had been at Nauset about a week there was a big thunderstorm one afternoon. Then the sun came out again just before it set. Johnny was sitting in front of his foster parents' house. Suddenly he heard a commotion, and looking up saw Squanto in his English clothes. Most of the Nauset Indians were gathered about him talking excitedly, but he saw Johnny and nodded to him.

Then Aspinet, the sachem, came up, and the two men talked. Johnny, his mouth wide open, listened. He heard Massasoit's name. Massasoit was the head sachem of all the Indians. Even Johnny knew that. Perhaps it was Massasoit who had let the English know where Johnny was. And

now Squanto was saying "Bang! Bang!" like a
musket. That meant that Captain Standish would
come and shoot them if they tried to keep Johnny.

But Aspinet was giving orders. The Indians
crowded about Johnny, saying good-by, and many
of them hung their necklaces about his neck. He
had strings of shells and of bears' claws and of
wampum, and Aspinet's wife gave him a string of
big striped beads which must have come from one
of the trading ships. For the second time since
he had been lost, Johnny cried. He cried because
he was grateful. And his tears thanked them for
all their kindness.

All together the Nausets walked down to the
beach towards the sunset, which brightened the
water to orange and yellow. There must have
been a hundred people. Squanto held Johnny by
the hand. It was low tide, and the Plymouth
shallop seemed very dark, grounded quite a distance out in the bay. Half the people stayed on
the beach, but Aspinet and fifty of his warriors,
putting down their weapons, went out to the boat.
Aspinet carried Johnny through the shallows and
handed him, all hung with necklaces, to Master

Winslow in the boat, and then lifted Trojan in, too. Trojan had been swimming and shook himself, but no one seemed to mind. There were about ten white people and three Indians from Cummaquid in the shallop.

"Welcome, Cocksparrow," said Master Winslow. "Your outing seems to have done you no harm. If it were not for the color of your eyes and hair, I should think that they had given us a little Indian!"

Then he turned to thank Aspinet for the care he had taken of Johnny and gave him a knife, which was something the Indians always loved, having nothing but knives of stone or bone themselves. And then he gave another knife — not quite so good — to the older of the two Manomet men who had brought Johnny to Nauset.

"Tell Aspinet," he told Squanto, "to bring beaver skins with him and come with his people to Plymouth. We will trade with him."

Aspinet smiled when Squanto explained what the white man had said.

267

"We will come," he answered.

It was getting late now, and Master Hopkins' serving men hoisted the sail, dark against the last glow of light in the west over far-off Plymouth. Master Winslow pushed with an oar, and the shallop slowly moved out into the bay. All the Indians shouted, and the women on the shore began to dance and sing. Johnny could not see anyone clearly in the dusk, but he stood up in the boat and waved and shouted, "Good-by! Good-by!" When they came to Plymouth he would take them around and show them everything, and perhaps his father would fire his musket to astonish them.

Plymouth. Soon he would be home. Master Winslow had not been angry with him. Johnny overheard him say to Master Hopkins:

"Were it not for the boy's being lost, this chance for trade would not have come. Governor Bradford wishes to question him as to the ways of these people. He is the only one of us all who has lived with them."

Johnny sat for a little while in the bottom of the boat, with Trojan hugged close in his arms. The evening star hung large and yellow over the distant shore. There lay Plymouth. His father and mother would be waiting. And what stories he would have to tell them! Even the older children would want to listen to him now.

And on this pleasing thought, Johnny went to

sleep, and Trojan, with a contented sigh, curled closer to him and went to sleep, also.

WHAT HAPPENED?

Johnny was a Pilgrim boy. The Pilgrims had to be brave to cross the ocean so long ago. Johnny was brave, too. He found an Indian camp when he was lost.

At first he wasn't even homesick. But after he was at the Indian camp for a while, he wondered about home. What did he wonder about?

Then Squanto came. Squanto was an Indian friend of the Pilgrims. What did Squanto tell the Indians?

When Johnny returned to Plymouth, Master Winslow was not angry. You would think he would be. Johnny had not watched his way when he chased his dog. Why wasn't Master Winslow angry?

THINK IT OVER

Suppose you were lost in the woods. You wouldn't have Indians to help you. What would you do?

Nowadays not many boys and girls get lost in the woods. But boys and girls do get lost in the city. What would you advise a boy or girl to do if he were lost in the city?

269

WILDERNESS

Elizabeth Coatsworth

The axe has cut the forest down,
The laboring ox has smoothed all clear,
Apples now grow where pine trees stood,
And slow cows graze instead of deer.

Where Indian fires once raised their smoke
The chimneys of a farmhouse stand,
And cocks crow barnyard challenges
To dawns that once saw savage land.

The axe, the plow, the binding wall,
By these the wilderness is tamed,
By these the white man's will is wrought,
The rivers bridged, the new towns named.

BILL CODY
*Ingri and
Edgar Parin d'Aulaire*

In the far-off days when Buffalo Bill was a boy
the land west of the Missouri River still belonged
to the Indians. . . .

Bill grew up at the edge of the plains, in the
wilds of Kansas Territory. There his father had
settled with his family to trade with the friendly
Kickapoo Indians. Little Bill Cody did not go
to school, and he could neither read nor write.
But early he learned to aim and shoot his father's
gun. His father had taught him that, until law
and order came, a frontier boy must be able to
look after himself. His home was far from white
neighbors, but Bill was not lonely. Right by his
door went a bumpy road, cut through the grass
by the wheels of the wagons that crossed the
· plains. It was called the Oregon Trail. Some-

times a trader with Indian trinkets or trappers with bundles of precious furs came riding down the Oregon Trail and stopped to tell of their adventures. All through spring covered wagons with emigrants for the far West would stop at his door. . . .

The drivers of the wagons, the lusty bull-whackers, were singing and bragging and telling tall tales of Indian battles and buffalo hunts. They loved the plains and their adventures. When Bill was big he would be a plainsman and a bullwhacker too! Bill's playmates were Kickapoo Indian children. He frolicked and romped and hunted small game with them, and learned their games and their language.

He traded his brand-new buckskin for a little wild Indian pony, and so he had a horse of his own.

Sometimes he rode bareback, Indian-fashion, sometimes he rode with a saddle, and soon he rode as if he and the horse were one.

Before he was twelve he rode so well that he got himself a grown man's job with a train of ox-drawn wagons bound across the plains with cattle and supplies. First rode the wagon boss, scanning the land for signs of danger. Then came the bullwhackers, cracking their long whips so they could be heard for miles. Last came young Bill, riding in the dust, keeping the cattle together. All day long they rumbled along.

At night they made camp, sat around the fire, sang and told stories. Then they all rolled up in their blankets and went to sleep. The stillness was broken only by loud snores and howling coyotes. Life on the plains was wonderful, thought Bill. . . .

Bill made many trips across the plains and became a seasoned plainsman. Sometimes he and his wagon train had to turn back. Sometimes they got all the way to Fort Laramie. There the United States flag was waving proudly against the blue haze of the Rocky Mountains, and the travelers could rest while the soldiers kept watch. There Bill met Kit Carson, the most famous of all the great scouts of the West. He had led many scouting expeditions all the way to California. Keen-eyed Kit Carson took a liking to young Bill Cody, who worshipped him in return. He taught Bill to read the language of the plains. Each broken blade of grass, each stirring bush, had a message for those who could understand it.

Bill learned to spell out nature's hidden language, but words and letters he still could not read. At nearby Register Cliff he stood with shame and watched while the travelers from the covered wagons scratched their names on the rock. Little boys and girls could write. He could sign his name only with a cross. There was no way around. He had to get off his horse and sit on the school bench instead. And so, at last, he learned his A B C's. But as soon as he could write his name with a flourish, he was off for the wide-open spaces again. Now he signed up with the Pony Express.

Eighty-six young daredevil riders were hired to carry news and mail across plains and mountains. All along the westward trail a chain of stations was built, well stocked with fodder and fast ponies. The riders galloped from station to station. Bill was the youngest of them all. Swift as the wind he galloped off, the precious mail pouch over his saddle. At the end of his run another rider waited. Bill threw the mail to him and he sped off. In this way hard-riding boys and sweating ponies carried the mail in nine days from the Missouri to the Pacific.

But it happened sometimes that Bill found his station in ashes, the men killed by Indians, the ponies driven off. Then he must ride his tired pony on to the next station, dodging Indian arrows on the way. Once he rode more than three hundred miles in one stretch. . . .

While the riders of the Pony Express were speeding across mountains and plains, other men were struggling to put up telegraph wires across the country. Indians burned the poles, and buffaloes rubbed their backs against them until they toppled over. But new poles came up, and when Bill and his friends had been riding for two years, the line was completed. Almost before a pony could be saddled, the telegraph wires had carried the news from coast to coast. The days of the Pony Express were over. . . .

. . . For a while he drove a stagecoach. That was fun and well paid, too. He swung his whip and soared across the plains. He grew a long mustache and a short goatee and let his hair fall down over his shoulders. That was to tease the Indians who would never get that handsome scalp, he said. As in the old days, clouds raced over the endless sky, and prairie dogs came scurrying out of their burrows to scold intruders and

275

scramble into their holes again. But the wilderness of Bill's childhood had changed. Kansas had now become a state, and more and more people were moving in. . . .

But with growing fury the Indians looked at the white men who were taking their land and killing off their buffalo herd. Soon Indian war drums sounded all over the plains. Soldiers were sent out to protect the white men and drive the Indians off their ancient hunting grounds. Buffalo Bill was sorry for the Indians. But he knew that, vast as the plains were, there wasn't room for Indians and white men both. And as he knew the plains better than most other white men, he became an army scout. . . . He was full of cheer and good stories. He was seldom tired and never afraid. When nobody else dared ride with warnings to outlying forts, he rode alone. He tied himself to his horse so he wouldn't lose his mount if it stumbled into a prairie-dog hole in the dark and sent him flying. Without his horse a man was badly off on the plains. . . .

Even Buffalo Bill could lose his mount. But he never lost his way in the wilderness when he led the soldiers in pursuit of dodging Indians. His trained eyes saw each quiver of the sagebrush, each broken blade of grass. Where he led the way in his white buckskin suit, the soldiers followed. In fighting, too, he charged on ahead with arrows flying about his head. One day an arrow went straight through his hat. But Buffalo Bill had luck on his side. The arrow only scratched his scalp.

One tribe after another was rounded up and sent off to reservations. Soon the last hostile Indian was forced to move toward the setting sun.

Before long, settlers were plowing their fields where buffalo once had roamed. Law and order had come to Kansas. But Buffalo Bill was bored. One day as he dozed in the shade under a wagon, wondering what to do now, a shiny boot nudged him awake.

"Aha," said the little fat man to whom the boot

277

belonged, "so you are as handsome as they say you are brave. If you'll tell me your adventures, I'll write them in books and make you famous." That suited Buffalo Bill just fine. He liked very much telling tall tales about his adventures, and the little fat man was a very fast writer. Soon people all over the country were reading dime novels about Buffalo Bill and his amazing adventures, and wanted to see their hero in person. He went East to the big cities, he traveled North, he traveled South. He looked so brave and so handsome in his wide-brimmed hat and his snow-white buckskin suit that people came from far and near to look at him. They paid much money to see him shoot his gun and do his Wild West stunts. Buffalo Bill had hit gold. He went home and talked some of his hard-shooting, rough-riding friends from the plains into coming with him. He rounded up some Indians, too, and started a show of his own.

All over the United States — yes, even in Europe — people cheered when Buffalo Bill and his Wild West Show came to town. Children and grownups, plain people, lords and kings thronged to watch whooping Indians race their ponies in pursuit of

stagecoaches and covered wagons. Then, in a cloud of sawdust, gallant and handsome Buffalo Bill, followed by his Wild West riders, came to the rescue. . . .

For forty years Buffalo Bill traveled all over with his show. He, more than any other man, made the world aware of the romantic Wild West and the wonderful new lands west of the Missouri. He grew famous and rich, but still he could not stay contented for long away from the wide-open spaces of home. Home to him did not mean only the gently rolling hillocks in Kansas where his father's humble cabin stood, but all the vast expanse of the plains and mountains where he had roamed in his youth.

High up in Wyoming he built himself a fine ranch where his wife and his children could live in comfort. And there, not far from Yellowstone Park, he helped to found the beautiful town of Cody, named in his honor. Kansas, Nebraska, Wyoming, Colorado all vied with each other in claiming him as one of their own.

Buffalo Bill grew old, but as long as he lived his gun hand was steady, and he and his horse still

279

seemed to be one. He never grew tired of telling his tales of the days of his youth when the Wild West was wild. And when he died, old and full of years, he had chosen for himself as his last resting place the top of a mountain in Colorado, overlooking the plains he had loved so much.

WHAT HAPPENED?

Buffalo Bill learned to ride on a wild Indian pony. He was only twelve when he got his first job. What did he do?

Buffalo Bill was a grown man before he could write his own name. But he could read, although not in books. What did Buffalo Bill read?

When the days of the Pony Express and the stagecoach were over, Buffalo Bill had little to do. Then one day came a little fat man. What did the fat man ask Buffalo Bill to do?

After forty years of traveling with his Wild West Show, Buffalo Bill settled down in Wyoming. He started a new town, not far from Yellowstone Park. What was it called?

THINK IT OVER

Buffalo Bill's "trained eyes saw each quiver of the sagebrush, even broken blades of grass." Buffalo Bill had trained himself to see the story in land, mountain, and sky where other eyes saw nothing. So he saw the beauty of the land and the wonder of the mountain and the sky.

What do you see as you walk along each day? Perhaps you are a city boy or girl. Your trips to the open countryside may be few. Is there anything in your city which makes you feel good when you look at it? Are there buildings of good, strong shapes? Do the busy patterns of the streets tell you an exciting story? What else do you see in your city that is good and pleasing in its color, its sound, or its shape?

Of course, if you live in the open country, it will be easy to see the same beauty and wonder which Buffalo Bill saw. But do you see it? Do you walk to school? Or do you ride on the bus? What do you see which would have pleased Buffalo Bill?

LINCOLN

Nancy Byrd Turner

There was a boy of other days,
A quiet, awkward, earnest lad,
Who trudged long weary miles to get
A book on which his heart was set —
And then no candle had!

He was too poor to buy a lamp
But very wise in woodmen's ways.
He gathered seasoned bough and stem,
And crisping leaf, and kindled them
Into a ruddy blaze.

Then as he lay full length and read,
The firelight flickered on his face,
And etched his shadow on the gloom,
And made a picture in the room,
In that most humble place.

The hard years came, the hard years went,
But, gentle, brave, and strong of will,
He met them all. And when today
We see his pictured face, we say,
"There's light upon it still."

UNIT SIX

FARAWAY
PLACES

THE SEA

Annette Wynne

The sea that comes to meet my hand
Is rolling on some foreign land;
And some small child in that far place
Is looking out to see my face.

ZEBEDEE, FISHERMAN

Alice Dalgliesh

Zebedee lived in a little house by the Cove. The sea came almost to his front gate.

When he was not in school or asleep, there were two places where Zebedee could be found. One was the old white boat on the beach just below his own cottage. The other was the wharf where the fishing boats came and went. It was on the Bay of Fundy, just half a mile over the hill.

Everyone knew Zebedee because of his wide, cheerful smile and his very blue eyes. They were even bluer than the Bay of Fundy, and that is very blue indeed.

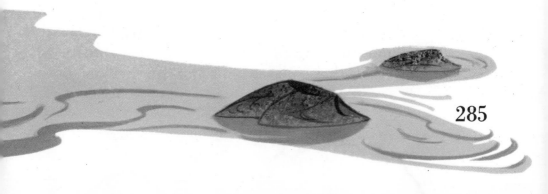

When people first met him they would say, "Zebedee? What a strange name for a little boy!" Zebedee did not mind having a strange name because in the first place everyone called him Zeb, and in the second place his mother had explained to him exactly how he happened to have that name. This is the story:

When Zebedee was born he was the only child in the family, so of course all the aunts and uncles and grandparents wanted to have something to say about his name. The aunts suggested "Earl" and "Everard" and "Leslie." The uncles suggested "John" and "Thomas" and "Richard." The baby's mother did not care for any of these names, nor did the baby's father. There was so much discussion over the naming of this blue-eyed scrap of a baby that, when the time came to take him to church to be baptized, nothing had been decided. This was very serious. The minister was waiting, and there was the baby in his long, white, embroidered christening robe. What was to be done?

"There is only one thing we can do," said Grandfather Harris. He sat down and took the family Bible on his knees. "The first name at which the Book opens shall be the child's."

Grandfather Harris put on his spectacles, opened the Bible, and ran his finger down the page. The aunts and the baby's mother held their breath, hoping that the name would not be Ezekiel or

Methuselah. Grandfather Harris cleared his throat importantly.

"It is a good name for a fisherman's son, for it was the name of a fisherman," he said. "The name is Zebedee."

Perhaps it was because of his name that Zebedee wished so much to be a fisherman. He loved the sea, he loved boats and fishing lines and rubber boots. He thought there was nothing in the world so interesting and exciting as fishing. It was interesting and exciting all the year round — spring, summer, and autumn.

In the spring it was lobster fishing.

All winter long there was a fence of lobster pots at one side of Zeb's house. In the spring Zeb's father piled all the lobster pots onto an ox cart and jogged slowly up to the Bay of Fundy. Zeb rode on the cart while his father walked

beside it.   Up the hill they went, past the pond, past Miss Letty's house, and down the steep hill to the wharf.   The oxen were so strong and sure-footed they did not seem to mind the heavy load of lobster pots or the rough road.

When the lobster pots were loaded on the boats, Zeb's father and the other fishermen pushed off, leaving him on the wharf.

"Lobster fishing is too cold for little boys," they said.

Zeb went home slowly and sadly.

In the summer Zebedee was almost always on the wharf, but the fishermen would not take him out with them.

"Little boys are a nuisance in boats," they said.

So Zeb watched the boats go out and walked on the wharf among the piles of cod that lay

drying in the sun. Sometimes the men would let him help to pile the dried fish into neat little rounded stacks, fish on fish, tail to tail. Zeb loved the smell of the salty, sun-dried cod.

When the fishing boats came in Zeb thought there was nothing more exciting than to help unload the piles of silvery cod and haddock, mackerel and pollock. When the fish were unloaded, Zeb and his father walked home, their rubber boots all covered with glistening scales, their rubber coats smelling beautifully of fish.

On autumn evenings when the moon was full, Zeb was sometimes allowed to stay up late and watch the fishermen drive the herring from Saint Mary's Bay into the Cove. Back and forth on the water darted the fishing boats, each with a great flaming torch at the bow. The herring came straight for the flares and soon the Cove was full of tiny fish, leaping from the water almost into the boats.

Zeb could scarcely stay on the wharf; he longed to have a net and scoop the herring into the boats. The fishermen would not take him out with them.

"It is dangerous for little boys when we have a torch in the boat," they said.

"It's always dangerous for little boys," said Zeb sadly.

At last, when Zeb was seven years old, his father took him fishing. Zeb had to wake up very early. He put on two pairs of stockings, two sweaters, and over the sweaters his rubber coat. Last of all he put on his mittens which were white as a fisherman's mittens must be. It was quite difficult to walk up the hill to the Bay of Fundy in all those clothes. The morning was cold and it was still almost dark. The wind moaned a little in the fir trees. Zeb began to wonder if he really wanted to be a fisherman.

As the boat pushed off from the wharf, Zeb began to feel more cheerful. When they were out in the bay and Zeb's own line slipped through his fingers into the dark, chilly water, he forgot all about the cold and the uncomfortable clothes. When his first fish, a big silver cod, lay in the bottom of the boat there was no happier boy in any fishing village from Sandy Cove to Tiverton.

290

Now fogs come in suddenly on Fundy, and before the fishermen knew it a thick white fog had blotted out the land. There was no beach to be seen, no bluffs, even the wharf had vanished. Perhaps they were opposite the wharf, perhaps they were nearer the wicked rocks just off the point.

They drifted, waiting for the fog to clear. The boat bobbed up and down on the water, and Zeb began to feel a little queer. His hands were cold, but he said nothing about it. He was sure it was hours before the fog lifted enough for them to see anything. Then the surprising thing was that, after all, they were only a few yards from the end of the wharf! How good the sturdy gray piles looked to Zeb! By the time he had climbed the ladder at the side of the wharf, and started up the hill, he began to feel better, though his head was dizzy and his legs were shaky. In his right hand Zeb carried the big silver cod, in his left hand a large pollock. His rubber boots were covered with glittering fish scales.

At the top of the hill Zeb and his father met Miss Letty's twins coming back from the village.

"Look!" said Zeb, holding up his fish. Abigail and Sara looked, and agreed that they were the finest fish that had ever come out of the Bay of Fundy.

A little farther down the hill, they met Miranda Saunders with a white kitten tucked under her arms. Miranda did not say a word, but Zeb knew that she wished she could go fishing.

When they reached the little house by the Cove, Zeb's mother was at the gate watching for him. A refreshing smell of dinner came through the front door. Zeb's mother admired the cod and the pollock.

"Weren't you afraid, out there in the fog?" she asked.

"No!" said Zebedee.

"Weren't you cold?"

"Not a bit!" said Zebedee, though his hands were blue.

"Or seasick?"

"Of course not"— although the ground on which

he stood had a curious way of coming up to meet him.

There was not the least doubt that Zebedee was a fisherman!

WHAT HAPPENED?

Zebedee was a strange name for a boy. Grandfather found the name. How did he find it?

For as long as he could remember Zebedee had wanted to go fishing with his father. His father kept saying he was too young. At last his father let Zeb go. What did Zeb wear to go fishing?

Zeb caught a big silver cod and a large pollock. He had been cold and just a little seasick. But he didn't tell anybody that — not even his mother. Why did he not tell anyone?

THINK IT OVER

Zebedee and his father fished off Newfoundland near the eastern shore of Canada. In the United States many men earn their living by fishing, too. Some of them may be near you. What do you know about fishermen in the United States? Do you know about the different kinds of fish they catch? What else can you find out about fishermen and fishing?

Do you ever go fishing? What kind of fish do you catch?

MAMA MIA'S BIRTHDAY

Brita Walker

The biggest event in the whole year for the
Angeletti family was Mama's birthday. Mama's
birthday came in August, the time of a great feast
in the church. Everywhere on every street people
were making preparations, and it seemed to Gino
and Maria that the preparations were specially for
Mama's birthday party, though they knew that
most of the people were really getting ready for
a great saint's day.

The Angeletti family lived in a big town by
the river between two great bridges. There was
Carmen who worked in the butcher shop, and
Jimmy who played the accordion, and Tom who
went to high school. And then there were Gino
and Maria. Gino was nine and Maria was seven,
the youngest and the only girl in the family.

The day Papa made the sausage for the great feast, Gino and Maria began to worry, for they knew that Mama's birthday wasn't far off. Papa always made the sausage for the feast. "Get out of the kitchen, all of you," he said. "I don't want any women spoiling my sausage."

Mama and Maria went into the parlor laughing, and in ten minutes Papa called, "Mama, get me the big pan in the pantry! Maria, I need all the spices! Where is the chopper and the garlic?" And before Papa knew it, everyone was back in the kitchen again.

Papa's big black mustache looked fine to Maria as she watched him. "When is the feast, Papa?" she asked.

"Soon, Maria, soon," Papa laughed. "I must hurry or the sausage will not be ready in time for it."

"How soon, Papa, how soon?" Gino asked, anxiously.

"In three days, Gino. Is it too long to wait?" Papa went on mixing his sausage. He didn't know that Gino and Maria were worried about getting a birthday present for Mama.

That very day Gino and Maria counted the pennies they had saved that summer. There were not very many.

"We have only twenty cents, Maria. That is not very much for a present for Mama." Gino looked sadly at Maria.

The children counted the money again. "Let's shine shoes, Gino. We can do that." The little girl with the shining eyes looked at her brother for approval.

"We can, Maria, we can. We can go by the steamboat dock. I'll get the polish and a box. You get a rag."

It wasn't ten minutes before the children were down by the steamboat dock. People were already waiting for the boat to come in.

At first Gino's "Shine, Mister?" was not very loud, but he wanted to buy Mama a present, and after a while he wasn't afraid. Not many people wanted their shoes shined, to be sure, but enough. Gino would put the polish on while Maria held the open can for him, and then Gino would rub the cloth on the shoes until they shone like new.

When the last of the passengers came off the boat that night, the children counted their money. They had nearly three dollars.

"We had better buy Mama some new polish," Gino said. "This can is empty."

The next morning Gino and Maria could hardly wait to walk along Main Street to see what they could find for Mama. They felt so rich and so proud. Three dollars was more money than either of them had ever earned before.

Main Street was a steep hill. Gino and Maria held hands as they walked.

In a furniture-store window they saw a big, comfortable rocking chair. "That would be fine for Mama," Maria said.

"It would be too expensive, Maria. We cannot get that."

At each store they stopped, Maria would put her face against the window and look. "There is nothing here, Gino, nothing for Mama."

They were almost at the top of the long hill. And then they saw what they wanted for Mama — RED SHOES!

Mama always wore black shoes. Red shoes would be just right for a party.

Gino and Maria opened the door with its tinkling bell. Gino held the money carefully in his hand. "How much do red shoes cost?" he asked.

"Two ninety-eight — on sale." The man looked at the children questioningly.

"We would like one pair," Maria said eagerly.

"What size?"

Gino looked at Maria and Maria looked at Gino. They had never thought about the size of Mama's shoes.

"I don't know," Gino said. "They are for Mama's birthday."

297

"I cannot sell you the shoes unless you find the size. Perhaps Mama has big feet — perhaps small." The man shrugged his shoulders.

Maria looked as if she might cry.

"If I brought one of Mama's old shoes to measure, would that be all right?" Gino was anxious.

"I guess so." The man turned away.

"You wait, Maria. I'll run home for Mama's shoes." Before Maria could speak, Gino ran out of the store as fast as his legs could carry him.

It seemed a long time to Maria before Gino came back, but suddenly, there he was, puffing from running up the hill. In one hand, he held Mama's oldest black shoe, in the other, still safely, the money for the red shoes.

The man looked at the shoe carefully while the children watched. "The size is almost impossible to see," he said at last, "but I guess I can find a pair about the same size."

He measured several pairs of red shoes with the old black one, and finally he was satisfied.

Gino and Maria felt extra happy as they walked into the house to hide their package for Mama's birthday party.

And now there was only one more day to wait. Colored lights were strung in all the streets. A great banging went on while the men made stands to hold the hot sausage and pizza that would be sold at the feast. Gino and Maria stood

watching, getting in the way. But no one grew angry. Everyone was happy because soon it would be "The Feast."

At home the preparations were tremendous. Mama was making all sorts of things for the dinner on the feast day. There would be spaghetti and chicken and ravioli and pizza and, of course, Papa's sausage. Maria and Gino helped with the stuffed celery, and washed the little after-dinner cups for coffee. Papa ordered a fine cake all decorated from the bakery. In no house were there so many things to be done. Everything shone for Mama's birthday and the feast.

That night it took a long while to go to sleep. Maria and Gino both were busy thinking about the next day. They heard many trains go by before they fell asleep.

In the morning they were up very early, but Mama was already in the kitchen making coffee for breakfast. Mama looked fine. Her best black dress was shining and lovely. Both children looked at Mama's feet.

"Black shoes," they thought. "Just wait until you see your birthday present."

"Happy birthday, Mama mia," Gino and Maria called together and kissed her.

299

"Thank you, Gino, Maria, and now hurry so we can all go to church."

Soon they were all out in the street together dressed in their very best — Papa and Carmen in their shining, black mustaches, Jimmy and Tom, and Gino and Maria and Mama. Mama's birthday, the feast day, always started with church and ended with church.

After church they all walked in the streets together to admire the booths with their gay articles for sale. They ate hot sausage, and Papa winked at Mama. "Not so fine as mine, eh, Mama?"

"No, Papa, but if you eat too much here, there will be no room for any when you get home."

Balloons and pinwheels, all kinds of things were being sold. Papa bought everyone something. Gino and Maria had red balloons which floated high above them as they walked along.

When they got home, Maria helped set the table and with Gino put the birthday package at Mama's place. Carmen brought his package and

300

Jimmy and Tom, and then Papa put two red roses and an envelope on the very top.

Gino and Maria could hardly wait for everyone to sit at the table. Before any food was brought in, they all watched Mama open the packages. Mama laughed as she pinned the red roses in her hair, and her cheeks grew pink. She thanked Papa for the flowers and the money for a new dress which she found in the envelope. She admired the new pocketbook from Carmen, the lovely slip from Jimmy, and the beautiful scarf from Tom, but it was Gino's and Maria's package that seemed best of all.

"Red shoes!" Mama said. "I never had red shoes. Oh, Gino and Maria, they are the finest present in the whole world!"

To everyone's surprise, except Gino's and Maria's, of course, the red shoes exactly fit, and Mama said she would wear them the rest of this gay day. Gino and Maria smiled all over, saying nothing at all until Carmen asked how Gino and Maria had saved so much money.

"We worked," Gino said.

"What did you do, Gino?" Papa sounded a little stern.

"We polished shoes at the steamboat dock. It did not take too long." For a minute Gino and Maria thought Mama and Papa were going to be angry, but Mama looked quickly at Papa, and Maria saw there were tears in her eyes.

301

"Do not scold the little ones," Mama said softly. "I never had such a fine present before."

WHAT HAPPENED?

Mama's birthday was almost here. Gino and Maria had only twenty cents. That wouldn't buy much of a birthday present. What did Gino and Maria decide to do?

Gino and Maria earned three dollars. Three dollars seemed like a lot of money. Yet it was not easy to find the right thing. Then they saw just what they wanted. What did Gino and Maria see?

The great day came at last. The whole family went to church. They visited the gay booths set up for the feast day. Then came the birthday party at home. Which present did Mama like best of all?

THINK IT OVER

Most families have their own ways to celebrate special days. Some families do special things for Easter. Some families have their own plans for the Fourth of July. Do you have special days to celebrate in your family? Or have you read about interesting things done by other families? What are some ways families celebrate special days?

302

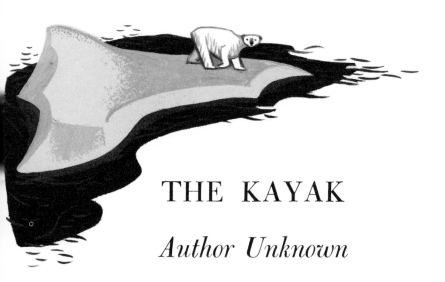

THE KAYAK

Author Unknown

Over the briny wave I go,
In spite of the weather, in spite of the snow.
What cares the hardy Eskimo?
In my little skiff, with paddle and lance,
I glide where the foaming billows dance.

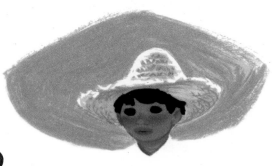

PANCHO

Berta and Elmer Hader

Don Fernando, the richest man in the village, was angry!

A wild bull with a crooked tail coaxed the best cattle in his herd to run away.

So Don Fernando offered a purse filled with gold to anyone who caught the bull with the crooked tail.

Cowboys from nearby ranches came to win the prize. First Alfonso rode out on the range. He was sure he would win the purse filled with gold.

But the wild bull ran away with Alfonso's broken lasso trailing from his horns. Alfonso went home.

"I'll win the prize," shouted Carlos as he galloped away in a cloud of dust.

Carlos lost his hat as well as his lasso, but he did NOT win the prize.

Then Jose, Juan, and Paco tried and failed. No one could catch the bull.

Don Fernando grew angrier and angrier. He offered a silver-trimmed saddle and the biggest hat in all Mexico as well as the purse of gold to anyone who caught the wild bull.

He put the prizes in the window of his store for everyone to see.

All the best riders on the finest horses in the whole state came to try to win the prize.

Every day these cowboys rode past the adobe hut where Pedro, the potter, lived with his wife and young son, Pancho. The little family made pots, plates, and bowls to sell in the village. Every morning Pancho led his little burro to the market place.

Pancho often stopped to look at the big hat and the saddle trimmed with silver in the window

of Don Fernando's store. No one wanted to win the reward more than Pancho. But he was only a little boy, and he had no swift horse or fine lasso with which to capture the wild bull.

Early one morning Pancho loaded his burro with all the pots his father had made and all the gay colored plates his mother had painted and set out for the market place. As he walked along he thought how fine it would be to ride in a saddle trimmed with silver, wearing the biggest hat in all Mexico, and how happy he could make his father and mother with the purse filled with gold.

"Heee-haw!" The burro stopped at the turn in the road and so did Pancho. Right in the middle of the road stood the WILD BULL with the crooked tail!

The cowboys' broken lassos trailed from his horns and he was angry.

Pancho turned about and the burro turned, too. They ran as fast as they could.

Whipped by the lassos, the bull ran after Pancho and the burro.

He knocked the pack from the burro's back! Pots, plates, and bowls rolled in all directions. The bull kept running, and Pancho felt his hot breath just as he scrambled to safety in a big oak that grew beside the road. The bull stamped on Pancho's hat and tossed his head. He snorted and bellowed. He was a very mad bull.

306

"VAMOS," shouted Pancho. But the bull would not go away. Pancho was a prisoner in the tree!

He wondered what to do. He looked at the lassos trailing from the bull's horns and thought hard.

Then he broke a hooked branch from the tree. Quickly he fished up the nearest lasso and fastened it firmly around the trunk of the tree. The bull pawed the ground angrily and moved closer.

Pancho fished up the other lasso and tied it firmly, too. Then he jumped to the ground and ran.

The bull charged after Pancho, but the lassos soon stopped him.

He bellowed and stamped his hoofs in a rage, but he could not get away. He was tied fast to the tree. The wild bull with the crooked tail was now a prisoner. Pancho caught his burro and hurried home to tell what had happened.

"MAMACITA, PAPACITO!" shouted Pancho, "I've caught the WILD BULL!"

His father and mother hurried down the road to see for themselves.

Just then Don Fernando and his cowboys came back from the cattle range. They stared at the bull tied to the tree, and they looked in amazement at Pancho and his burro. The news spread fast.

The mayor hurried to the oak tree followed by most of the villagers. It was true! Pancho,

307

the potter's son, had captured the wild bull with the crooked tail. The mayor proclaimed a holiday in honor of the occasion.

The next day Pancho wore the biggest hat in all Mexico and sat in a saddle trimmed with silver as he led the procession through the village streets and around the market place. Then Don Fernando gave him the purse filled with gold. "Viva, viva!" shouted the villagers. Pancho was happy.

With the gold in the purse, Pancho bought his father a motor car to ride in, and he bought a new dress and a bright red shawl for his mother. They were all very happy.

Now that his cattle were safe Don Fernando was happy, too.

Everyone was happy except the wild bull with the crooked tail. He had to stay in a pen with a brass ring in the end of his nose.

WHAT HAPPENED?

The wild bull with the crooked tail just could not be caught. Alfonso tried. Carlos tried. Many others tried. Nobody thought Pancho could catch the bull. Why did no one think that Pancho could catch the bull?

The wild bull knocked all the pots, plates, and bowls from Pancho's burro. Pancho ran for a safe place. Where did Pancho find a safe place?

The bull stamped and snorted. Then Pancho had an idea. He would use those broken lassos still tied to the wild bull. How did Pancho use the broken lassos to catch the wild bull?

Don Fernando was very happy. The wild bull with the crooked tail was caught at last. What did Don Fernando give as a reward to Pancho?

THINK IT OVER

Pancho's story tells you something about Mexico and its people. What else do you know about Mexico? Have you ever been there? Have you ever read about Mexico? What else would you see if you were in Mexico?

COW BELLS SING

Earle Goodenow

A small mountainside farm in Switzerland dozed in the early morning twilight. Inside the chalet a little girl slept. Her lips curved in a smile as she dreamed, and the corners of her eyes crinkled merrily.

Outside, the sun was just poking its nose over the mountains to the east. It threw a long golden shaft across the valley. It gilded the steep slopes and meadows of the farm. It touched the roof of the house and moved down to the balcony. Then it entered the room and kissed the little girl on the end of her nose.

She opened her eyes and sat up. Then she started to laugh. She washed and dressed and pulled on her stockings and shoes quickly. She was still laughing when she kissed her mother and father at the breakfast table.

"I just had the silliest dream," she told them. "All our cows were singing and dancing and playing tunes on their bells."

"What fun!" chuckled her mother.

"Humph," said her father.

After breakfast Marie-Louise went into the parlor to play the piano. She played very well because she loved music and practiced whenever she could.

Presently she went out and stood by the pasture gate. She looked down toward the town, and in the clear summer air the houses looked like toys. From where she stood it was a toy train that wound along the valley floor, and toy cows dotted the far slopes.

The air was filled with familiar sounds. The train's whistle drifted up from far below. The chickens clucked as they scratched and pecked in the grass. A church bell tolled softly in the distance, and from far and near came the murmur of other bells. This was the sound of the herds, for every cow in the valley wore a bell.

They were like ordinary bells attached to broad leather straps around the necks of the animals. The heavy clappers that hung inside banged

against the edges when the cows moved. But they were all sizes. Some were small, and some were middling, and some were nearly as big as bushel baskets.

Marie-Louise had few playmates, so she had made friends with her father's cows.

First there was Berthe, who was the oldest. Then there were Yvonne, Celine, Jeanne, Francoise, Helene, Bettine, Henriette, Bernice, Paulette, and Nicole. And last, but far from least, there was Fat Annette.

Marie-Louise loved them all. She talked to them and sang to them, and they loved her in return. So when they saw her standing there they came over to say good morning.

"Did you sleep well, darlings?" she asked.

They bobbed their heads. All except Fat Annette who was occupied with a thick tuft of grass. Berthe nudged her sharply, and Annette looked up and nodded so vigorously that her bell rang like thunder.

"That's all right, Annette," said Marie-Louise, smiling. "I know you're always hungry, so go right ahead." And Annette gratefully plunged her nose into the grass again.

Berthe moved up to the gate and stood invitingly beside it. She was the quietest of them all, and sometimes Marie-Louise rode on her back. So now she climbed aboard.

At first Berthe paraded slowly and proudly across the pasture, but this morning she just felt too good to go slow. Before long she was galloping around the field with the others clanking and clanging happily beside her.

Marie-Louise was delighted. She shouted with laughter and called to her father to look. But the bells made such a deafening uproar that no one could hear anything else. She covered her ears to keep out the racket.

Berthe finally came to a stop before Marie-Louise's father who had come to see what the commotion was about.

"Oh, Papa," gasped the little girl as she slid off into his arms, "did you ever hear such a terrible noise?"

He looked at her slyly.

"Fine tunes they play on their bells!" he said, and went away laughing.

Marie-Louise's ears rang all the rest of the day from the din. They even rang as she lay in her bed that night trying to sleep. Then suddenly she had an idea.

She sat up straight in the dark.

"Why didn't I ever notice it?" she said out loud. "The bells on our cows have notes just like our piano. All the notes in the scale! I'm going to teach them to make music instead of just noise!"

Next morning she took her old phonograph out onto her balcony. The cows lined up quietly along the fence below, staring up at her.

She put on her favorite record, "The Blue Danube." But when the music came out of the big horn the cows were quiet no longer. Their feet tapped and their heads bobbed and suddenly they were jumping and rolling all over the pasture.

Yvonne danced on her hind legs. Helene stood on her forelegs and Fat Annette fell over

backwards with a thump that shook the house. Even the chickens were hopping up and down.

"Goodness!" exclaimed Marie-Louise when the piece was over. "They surely like it, but I'll have to find a better way to teach them how to play."

She went downstairs and took a sheet of music from the piano and a twig from the kindling box by the fireplace.

"I think one note at a time will be better," she said to herself as she went out to the pasture.

She lined up all the cows according to the notes of their bells. It was quite a task. While she was getting them seated, Helene stepped on Paulette's tail and promptly started to run away as Paulette scrambled to her feet. They went around the pasture three times before Marie-Louise could get them to come back and sit peaceably.

It wasn't easy teaching the cows to shake their bells one at a time and only when she pointed her stick. They would ring out of turn or suddenly feel silly and not move at all. Fat Annette simply couldn't resist a nice bunch of grass, and didn't even see Marie-Louise point at her half the time.

It was very discouraging.

But they tried very hard to please their mistress, and as the days passed they gradually caught on. They would sit in a semi-circle around her, each one waiting for Marie-Louise's signal to shake her head and make her bell ring.

315

Soon they could tell they were making a pleasant noise when they followed her little stick.

When winter came the cows stayed in the barn all the time, but the hours passed pleasantly. Marie-Louise was with them whenever her father wasn't around, and they became very skilled at their music.

It was cozy and warm there. The chickens scratched in the straw on the floor, and between pieces the cows munched hay in their mangers.

One day Marie-Louise was looking out the window.

"It's beautiful outside," she told them. "Everything is white. The mountains and the valley and the pastures. The chalet looks like a cake with three feet of marshmallow frosting on top. Wouldn't you like some of that?"

She was sorry she had said that. Annette was staring out the window so hungrily that Marie-Louise knew she'd be no good for the rest of the day.

The sun grew warmer, and the snow began to melt. In the valley the ground showed dark more and more. Spring had come.

The cows could now play "The Blue Danube" and three other Strauss waltzes, and they were learning the "Moonlight Sonata" and the "Swiss National Anthem."

One afternoon Marie-Louise's father was taking a nap in the hayloft when he was awakened by the music. From where he was he could look down and see some of the cows, but he couldn't see Marie-Louise. He listened in surprise until they had finished their piece. Then he rushed out of the barn to the house.

"I've just had the craziest dream!" he told his wife. "The cows were all playing a Strauss waltz on their bells."

"Humph," said his wife.

By the time summer came again the cows knew all their music by heart. They were so pleased with themselves that even Fat Annette could be counted on to pay attention.

WHAT HAPPENED?

Marie-Louise lived high in the mountains of Switzerland. She liked the cows with their bells of different sizes. One of the cows was always eating. Which cow was that?

Papa gave Marie-Louise an idea. All through the winter Marie-Louise played music for the cows. She taught the cows to watch her stick. What was each cow supposed to do when Marie-Louise pointed the stick?

One afternoon while Papa was sleeping he had the craziest dream. He ran to tell his wife. What was Papa's dream?

THINK IT OVER

You've seen Donald Duck and Woody Woodpecker do strange and wonderful things in the movies or on television. The story of Marie-Louise and her musical cows might make a good cartoon movie. Suppose you were making the movie. You would need to have some good scenes to show the mountains and the farm settled down among the mountains. What would the mountains and the farm look like in your movie?

You would need to show Marie-Louise and Papa and Mama. How old would Marie-Louise be? What would Papa and Mama look like?

Of course, you would need to show those wonderful cows in your movie. Not all the cows would be alike. Some might be very bright. Some might not be so bright. Some might be funny. How would the cows act?

318

UNIT SEVEN

A LONG STORY

THEIR
FIRST IGLOO

Barbara True and

Marguerite Henry

Their First Igloo by Barbara True and Marguerite Henry, originally titled *Their First Igloo on Baffin Island.* By permission of the publishers, Albert Whitman & Company.

THE GOOD SEASON RETURNS

Thick, fat flakes of snow were falling over the sober brown earth far up the map on Baffin Island. The Eskimos grinned with joy. Everyone was glad to have the treeless land covered with clean white snow.

Even the dogs were glad. They frisked and leaped into the air, snapping at the snowflakes as they fell.

The boy, Nuka, and the girl, Palea, ran up and down the gravelly shore. "Winter is here!" they shouted. "The good season is here!"

Palea followed close in Nuka's footsteps. She was smaller and younger than Nuka, but nobody knew their exact ages. Eskimos do not celebrate birthdays. Years are not important to them. Skill and bravery are the things that really matter.

Kingmik, the children's Husky dog, raced back and forth between the chained Huskies and the children. Kingmik liked the taste of the fresh snow on her tongue. She was about ten moons old now, neither puppy nor grown dog.

The wind was blowing strong and cold. Nuka turned his face to the slanting snow. "The caribou will be heading toward the sun," he said. "Perhaps this year I will really shoot a fine buck with my bow and arrows."

"Perhaps," replied Palea, thinking only of the endless amount of sinew she would have to pluck apart into sewing thread.

"Come, Palea!" called Nuka. "Let us go back to the tent. Surely we will be traveling toward The Shadows now."

Eskimos have a pleasant way of naming directions. To travel north is to go toward The Shadows. To travel south is to go toward The Sun.

Palea poked her merry brown face inside the tent. "Nuka and I," she sang out, "should like to help with the packing."

But there were no signs of packing. Papa Eskimo was drawing symbols on a piece of skin with a sharp black stone. Mamma was putting a new spear head on her harpoon. And in the corner, the little old grandmother sat shivering, as she patiently scraped a caribou skin to make it soft.

322

At the sound of Palea's voice, a black-eyed baby peered out of the mother's hood and gurgled.

Nuka and Palea exchanged troubled glances. Weren't they ever going to travel again? Now was the time to return to the frozen sea for the winter. Everyone else in the camp had left after the first snow. That was many sleeps ago.

The children knew better than to ask questions. Eskimos consider it rude to pry answers out of people. When Little Grandmother felt strong enough, perhaps they would go.

Papa chuckled. "One or two sleeps, my little ptarmigans, and we will head for The Shadows." Papa liked to call the children ptarmigans. They are the funny Arctic birds that wear white feathers in winter and brown ones in summer.

"Soon," Papa went on, "the snow will be packed firm and hard, and the going will be good. One would not want little Kingmik here to be lost in a snowdrift."

Kingmik whined almost as if she understood, and her tail thumped noisily against the frozen ground.

"Kingmik is trained to break the trail," Papa continued in his story-telling voice. "She will be a brave lead dog. But if you make a pet of her, she will not mind her master."

The family burst into laughter. Kingmik was already a pet. It was too late to change that. Ever since her puppy days when the children carried her around in Papa's old mitten, she had been a pet. Nuka tweaked her one black-tipped ear and smiled at her wise little face.

The snow began sifting into the tent, and the chill wind whistled through the seams. Oh, it would be good to live in a snug, warm igloo again.

ON TOWARD THE SHADOWS

All day and all night the snow fell silently. Then late the next morning, a sliver of sun peeped up over the horizon. Palea and Nuka nodded their heads with glee. Now they would

go. Now the snow was packed firm and hard, and the wind was still. Now Little Grandmother could stand the journey.

Proudly Mamma brought out the new suits she had made. The children pulled on their inner coats. How silky they felt! It was pleasant to wear them fur side in. There were new deerskin stockings too, and hightop boots called *mukluks*.

But most beautiful of all were the fur parkas. Each parka had enormous sleeves so that frostbitten hands could be pulled up inside where it was cozy and warm.

Outdoors, two sleds were waiting to be packed. One was big and old and travel-scarred. The other was small and new.

The air was brisk with excitement. The dogs howled. Mamma whisked in and out of the tent, carrying sleeping bags, rifles, harpoons, snowshoes. Even Grandmother helped with the lighter bundles.

325

The children packed all of their own treasures on the small sled. Nuka brought out his bow, and some flint for arrowheads. Palea carried her stone lamp with the dried moss for a wick, and the seal blubber to make a good light. Then came the very best part of the load — a day's supply of delicious frozen fish.

When the packing was nearly done, Nuka's snow-knife could not be found. With head held low, Nuka admitted he had left it outside the tent, and that now it must be buried deep in snow.

This was a serious matter. Yet the grownups neither scolded nor frowned. With good-natured smiles, everyone began digging for the knife. At last, with a chuckle of delight, Mamma found it.

Now they were almost ready. The tent was laced to the large sled, and Papa was covering the bulging load with bearskins.

"Come, Tekegak!" shouted Papa. "Come, Amalai! Naluk! Melik! Kernek . . ." One by one Papa and Nuka called their dogs to be harnessed. Only Kingmik and Eema, the lead

326

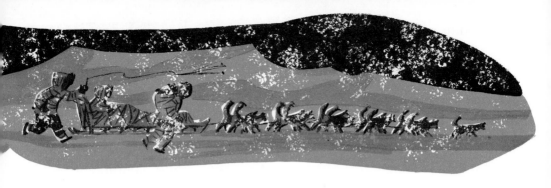

dogs for each team, were left free. Papa led them to the river and chopped a large hole. Then the dogs lapped the black water flowing beneath the ice. This would help them follow the river trail.

Gently, Little Grandmother was lifted onto the big sled. Her black eyes smiled at the thought of going toward The Shadows.

"*Ak-su-sé!* Be brave, my little ptarmigans!" called Papa, "and keep close behind us."

Papa's great long whip cracked in the frosty air, and the big sled was off. Both Papa and Mamma ran alongside, and the baby joggled along in Mamma's hood.

Nuka waited only a little. Then he too cracked his whip, and his dogs, barking and yelping, spread out fanwise over the snow. The children ran alongside their sled, just like Papa and Mamma.

The sled moved slowly at first, then faster and faster. Oh, it was fun to hear the squeaky music of the runners, and to see the clean, white snow stretching away to the horizon!

327

LOST!

Overhead, the plane of a white man purred as it headed toward The. Sun. Palea and Nuka shouted, but up ahead Kingmik never glanced at that noisy creature in the sky. She seemed to know she was responsible for the way. Her bushy plume of a tail waved importantly.

The little sled followed the tracks of the big sled for a long, long time. Occasionally Palea would climb on top of the load and snuggle into the warm furs for a doze.

If the dogs were pulling uphill, Palea and Nuka helped push the sled. Then laughing and breathless, they would hop onto the load and swoop downhill to the merry squeaking of the runners and the barking of the dogs.

Near the North Pole the days get shorter in the fall until, in mid-winter, there is no day at all. Nuka was not surprised at the early twilight. But suddenly he realized that what he thought to be the big sled was only shadowy darkness. Were there no rocks?

328

He looked around for a familiar rock. There
was nothing; nothing but the thick, white snow.

As he glanced up at the gray sky, fresh
snowflakes touched his face. Instantly they came
thicker and thicker, whirling and drifting until
he could not see his own boots. Blindly he ran
ahead of the dogs. If there had been any tracks
of the larger sled, they were gone now, filled in
with fresh snow.

Palea, on top of the load, was awakened by the
sting of wind and snow. She jumped down and
stumbled along beside the sled, keeping close to
Nuka.

"Nuka, oh, Nuka!" she called.

Nuka bent close to hear.

"Nuka," she repeated weakly, "an igloo would

be very nice right now." She had meant to cry
out, "Are we lost? Oh, are we lost?" But the
question never came.

Nuka grinned to hide his fear. He cracked his
whip and shouted "Hoo!" The dogs stopped in
their tracks. Already those nearest the sled had
heard the welcome word *igloo*.

Dusk was deepening. Nuka would have to
build fast, for unless the air cleared there would
be no moon nor stars. He reached for his snow-
knife. A quiver of excitement ran up and down
his spine. This would be his first igloo without
Papa.

"Wait here, Palea," he directed, "I will take
Kingmik with me to find more solid snow."

Nuka called for Kingmik, but there was no
rush of white fur. The only answer was the
hungry whining of the harnessed dogs.

"Kingmik! Kingmik! Oh, Kingmik!" The cries
filled the air.

"She was still a puppy," said Nuka hoarsely,
"and we have lost her."

When Nuka began strapping on his snowshoes,
Palea knew he was going after Kingmik. "I will
go, too," she announced.

"No, Palea," said Nuka firmly. "You will be
my anchor. I will keep calling to you, and you
must call back. I will go only as far as I can
hear you call."

Nuka started back over the snow-filled tracks,

330

calling anxiously for Kingmik. Then he would call to Palea. Always she answered in her firm, high voice. He trudged on, hopefully at first. There had never been another soft, wriggling puppy like Kingmik.

If only, thought Nuka, Kingmik could have remained a puppy always, small enough to stay in Papa's caribou mitten forever.

Palea's answers were growing fainter. Nuka suddenly felt cold and tired, and not very brave. He turned back, alone, into the teeth of the storm. He was glad when he found Palea safe.

THE FIRST IGLOO

Meanwhile Palea had been figuring things out. "If we stay here," she told Nuka, "Kingmik will catch up with us."

Nuka nodded. He would try to believe that, too. Without a word he began testing the snow for firmness. Not far from the sled he found a place swept clean of drift. Skillfully he cut a neat snowblock. Then he cut another and another and another. He placed them around him in a small circle.

Steadily Palea held the blocks while Nuka beat them in place. Then she filled the little cracks between with snow. Nuka was working on the inside, building the house around him. As each row went up, he trimmed the blocks so that the igloo became as round as a beehive. Soon he was setting the last block into place at the top of the dome.

When the house was finished, Nuka shoved one block aside for the doorway. Then out he crawled on all fours, like a polar bear lumbering out of a cave.

"A warm igloo," he laughed, proud of his skill.

Palea was not to be outdone. She ran for her stone lamp. In it she placed some dry moss and a piece of seal blubber. Then she crawled into the house and lighted the moss with flint. The flame flickered and soon filled the igloo with comfort.

"Why, Nuka!" she cried, "you have even built the little sleeping bench."

Palea covered the bench with bearskins and deerskins, and the house began to look very much like home. Then she put a chunk of ice in her sealskin bucket and hung it over the lamp. When it melted they would have good water to drink.

Out in the blizzard Nuka unharnessed the dogs and fed them each a large slice of frozen fish. Then he made little hollows in the snow where they could sleep for the night.

In silence Palea and Nuka ate their share of the frozen fish. Their minds kept going back to Kingmik. "If she should come now," said Palea, "there would be no food for her."

"After a sleep," replied Nuka, "I shall hunt, and we shall *all* feast." His words sounded more cheerful than his voice.

While the snow whirled about their igloo, Palea chewed their dried boot soles to make them soft and silky again. Nuka was busy making many arrows and many plans. "When Kingmik finds us," he said wishfully, "we will go on. We will find a village, or someone traveling who may have seen Mamma and Papa."

The seal-oil lamp threw funny black shadows on the snow walls. Palea watched them and her eyes grew heavy. She dimmed the light and crawled into her sleeping bag.

Nuka went out to call once again for Kingmik. A blast of wind and snow whirled into the igloo. At last he came back, and he, too, crawled into his sleeping bag.

Somewhere a wolf howled. Palea and Nuka

snuggled deep down in their furs and dreamed
of Mamma and Papa and a fine igloo with many
passageways.

THE CARIBOU COME

Palea awoke with a start. What was that
rustling noise?

Cautiously she looked up through the little
ventilation hole in the dome of the igloo. There
she saw the quivering glow of the northern lights.
She laughed with relief.

"Look, Nuka!" she called. "Awake quickly. The
Good Shadows have come."

Both children slipped into their fur suits and
went out into the cold stillness. The snow had
stopped, and the air was alive with color. It was
like the sight of many rainbows. But these were
not quiet, peaceful bands across the sky. They
crackled. They danced. They swirled and
twisted. They flamed bright, then faded, then
flamed again. Above and around them, cold white
stars pricked the blackness of the sky.

Nuka and Palea watched as if they were bewitched by the shimmering magic. Suddenly a small group of caribou stood out against the light.

Nuka ran back into the igloo, stumbling over the little snowy hummocks where the dogs lay deep in slumber. Out he came with his bow and arrows. "We must reach the caribou before the Good Shadows are gone," he breathed.

The sharp air hurt their lungs, but Nuka and Palea ran swiftly. Caribou meant food for Kingmik, and food for themselves.

The animals were galloping toward them now, galloping toward the sun, even as Nuka had said. Nuka dropped to his knee and shot an arrow. It sailed over the antlers of the caribou.

The animals stopped in their tracks and gazed with curiosity at the young hunter. They came nearer and nearer. These were the small Arctic caribou, but to Nuka they looked like giants.

Again Nuka took aim. This time his shaft went whistling into the air and hit a big buck. The other animals bolted, but the buck suddenly staggered and fell in a heap.

335

The children hopped and danced with joy. "Oh, Nuka!" cried Palea. "We will have tender, sweet meat to eat, and I will sew you the most beautiful *mukluks* in the world."

Together Palea and Nuka dragged the animal close by the igloo. There they skinned and cleaned it and built an Eskimo cache over the meat. An Eskimo cache is an ice box actually made of ice.

So busy were the children that they did not hear sounds far off. Finally their dogs shook themselves out of their snowy quilts and began to bark.

"It seems as if those are good noises," said Nuka.

"I hear them too," nodded Palea.

The northern lights were dying now. Their pale yellow glow painted the whole world the color of a walrus tusk.

"Nuka!" exclaimed Palea. "Do you see that dark spot on the horizon? What do you suppose it can be?"

"Often we see sleds coming, and first they are only dots."

"Perhaps it is nothing at all, but it does seem bigger than it was. It *is* bigger," shouted Palea. "I see a sled, and I see two people running alongside, and — oh, Nuka, I see — "

Palea was interrupted by the exciting yelping of a white dog with one black-tipped ear. Across

336

the snow she whizzed, her plume of a tail whipping from side to side. With a bark of joy she pounced first on one child and then the other. She nuzzled their familiar faces with her cold nose.

All the while she whined in little syllables. It seemed as if she was trying to tell them of all the longing and worry that one Eskimo puppy could suffer for two people she loved.

"Hoo!" shouted Papa, and the big sled came to a sudden stop. Papa's face was creased with smiles. He chuckled and laughed as only Papa could.

"We have come!" he announced. "Kingmik did not obey her driver, but —" and here Papa's black eyes twinkled, "I say again, she is a great lead dog. When your team could not pull against the storm, Kingmik came to the village and led us to where you were."

"Eh-h-h," nodded Mamma, pressing her cheek against Palea's and Nuka's.

Papa was looking at the igloo. "It is good," he said, as he walked right over the frozen dome to test its strength. "It is good."

"Nuka is a hunter too," whispered Palea as she pulled Papa over to the cache.

When Papa saw the fine big caribou, he chuckled with pride. "Indeed he is a brave hunter! Won't Little Grandmother be proud, too!"

Laughing and joking they all packed the

children's sled. Now the whips cracked, and the dogs leaped into action. Both Nuka and Palea looked back just once at their first igloo. Then they turned their faces toward The Shadows.

OH, KINGMIK!

Before another sleep they reached the village. There were so many igloos that the frozen sea looked like a big plate of marshmallows.

At the barking of the dogs, men, women, and children rushed out of the igloos as thick as snowflakes. Such shouts of welcome!

Old friends unhitched both dog teams and anchored them for the night. They even unpacked the sleds.

Then came the feast of Nuka's caribou. But instead of lasting for hours, the party was over all too quickly. The guests ate some meat, but each carefully hid a delicious morsel in his hand. Then, one by one, they made excuses to leave.

When all the guests had gone, Palea and Nuka hurried out to Kingmik. For a whole day they had carefully saved the heart of the caribou for her. This was the choicest, most toothsome part of the feast.

"Won't she leap for joy!" whispered Palea.

But Kingmik did not leap. She lay in a snow hollow, curled up in a ball. No amount of shaking would rouse her. She pretended not to hear. She hardly sniffed the meat at all.

338

Palea and Nuka were worried. In all her life, Kingmik had *never* refused to eat. They carried her into their igloo. How heavy she seemed.

And then, in the flickering light of the seal-oil lamp, Palea and Nuka laughed until the tears rolled down their round, brown faces. They stroked Kingmik's bulging sides. "So that's where all the tasty snacks have gone! That is why our guests left so slyly."

Kingmik hiccuped.

"It is good we do not have to break the trail tonight," said Papa. "Kingmik would have to ride on top of the load."

And the whole family laughed and laughed until the sounds of their laughter fluttered through the passageway and out into the starry night.

WHAT HAPPENED?

Papa said that soon the Eskimo family would head for The Shadows. What was the reason for waiting?

Off they went, finally. Papa drove the big sled, and Nuka drove the little sled. Trouble came with early twilight. What was the trouble?

Kingmik was only a puppy. And she, too, was lost somewhere out in the snow. Nuka went out to look for the dog. What did Palea do?

Nuka worked fast to build an igloo. Palea

339

helped as best she could. When the igloo was done, Palea ran to get a light. What kind of light did she bring?

That night Palea saw that the "Good Shadows" had come. They danced like magic in the sky. What is another name for the "Good Shadows"?

Just as the "Good Shadows" were leaving the sky, Nuka and Palea heard sounds in the distance. The sounds came nearer and nearer. Then an object came whizzing over the snow. What was it?

Back in the village the people ate the good meat which Nuka had brought. The villagers saved some of the meat to give away. Who was given the meat?

THINK IT OVER

Nuka and Palea proved themselves to Papa and all the villagers. Boys and girls like to prove themselves. They like to show parents and other grownups that they can be brave and strong.

Probably not many of you have had to face danger as Nuka and Palea did. But there are other ways of proving yourself. Some of you are traffic guards at school. You see that younger boys and girls cross streets safely. You prove yourself by showing that others can depend on you. What else can you do to show that others can depend on you?

340

DICTIONARY

This dictionary will help you to understand and pronounce some of the more difficult words in ALONG THE SUNSHINE TRAIL. Words are explained according to the way they have been used in the selections. Sometimes a word has been used two different ways. In such cases two meanings are given. At the bottom of each page is a key to pronunciation.

A

absurd (ăb·sûrd′), *adj.* Silly; foolish.
actually (ăk′tū·ȧl·ē), *adv.* Really; truly.
adobe (ȧ·dō′bē), *n.* Sun-dried brick used to make houses.
adopt (ȧ·dŏpt′), *v.* To take and treat as one's own.
advise (ȧd·vīz′), *v.* To tell someone what should be done.
agate (ăg′ĭt), *n.* A hard stone with stripes of color.
alert (ȧ·lûrt′), *adj.* Wide-awake and quick acting.
aloft (ȧ·lôft′), *adv.* High up.
ambitious (ăm·bĭsh′ŭs), *adj.* Having the feeling that one would like to do more and better.
ample (ăm′p'l), *adj.* More than enough; plenty.
ancient (ān′shĕnt), *adj.* From times long ago.
approach (ȧ·prōch′), *v.* To come toward.
approval (ȧ·prōōv′ȧl), *n.* Praise; agreement.
armor (är′mẽr), *n.* Metal covering used to protect the body.
astonished (ȧs·tŏn′ĭsht), *adj.* Surprised.
atmosphere (ăt′mŏs·fẽr), *n.* The air around the earth.
attentive (ȧ·tĕn′tĭv), *adj.* Listening and watching closely.
auction (ôk′shŭn), *n.* A public sale.
authority (ô·thŏr′ĭ·tē), *n.* A person who knows more about something than most other people do.
avoid (ȧ·void′), *v.* To keep away from.

ā, āte	ä, ärm	ē, mē	ĕ, ĕnd	ī, īce	ōō, fōōd
ă, ăm	ȧ, ȧlive	ê, rêturn	ē, bakẽr	ĭ, ĭll	ŏŏ, fŏŏt

B

barometer (bȧ·rŏm′ė·tēr), *n.* An instrument that shows changes in the weather.

bass (bās), *adj.* Low and deep in tone.

bewildered (bė·wĭl′dērd), *adj.* Surprised and confused.

billows (bĭl′ōs), *n.* Big waves.

binding (bīn′dĭng), *v.* Holding together.

blare (blȧr), *v.* To make a loud noise.

booth (bōōth), *n.* A small counter where things are sold.

borne (bôrn), *v.* Carried.

braced (brāst), *v.* Supported or held up.

brindle (brĭn′d′l), *adj.* Gray or brown with dark spots.

briny (brīn′ē), *adj.* Salty.

burrow (bûr′ō), *n.* A hole in the ground used by a small animal as a home.

C

calamity (kȧ·lăm′ĭ·tē), *n.* A very bad happening.

calico (kăl′ĭ·kō), *n.* A cotton cloth.

calmly (käm′lē), *adv.* Without excitement; quietly.

chalet (shă·lā′), *n.* A small wooden house found in Switzerland.

chink (chĭngk), *n.* A crack.

clatter (klăt′ēr), *n.* Mixed noises.

clearance (klēr′ȧns), *n.* Space in which to move about.

coax (kōks), *v.* To tease someone to do something.

cockpit (kŏk′pĭt), *n.* The place where the pilot sits in an airplane.

commotion (kŏ·mō′shŭn), *n.* Noise and disorder.

confound (kŏn·found′), *v.* To amaze or greatly surprise.

consolingly (kŏn·sōl′ĭng·lē), *adv.* Comfortingly.

contradict (kŏn·trȧ·dĭkt′), *v.* To say the opposite of what has already been said.

conversation (kŏn·vēr·sā′shŭn), *n.* Talk.

cordial (kôr′jăl), *n.* A sweet drink made from fruits.

courtier (kōr′tĭ·ēr), *n.* One who serves the king.

cradle (krā′d′l), *n.* The framework which holds a rocket ship.

ā, āte	ä, ärm	ē, mē	ĕ, ĕnd	ī, īce	ōō, fōōd
ă, ăm	ȧ, ȧlive	ē, rēturn	ē, bakēr	ĭ, ĭll	ŏŏ, fŏŏt

crater (krā′tēr), *n.* A big hole in the ground.
croak (krōk), *v.* To speak in a low, hoarse way.
crotch (krŏch), *n.* The place where two tree limbs meet.
crystal (krĭs′tȧl), *n.* 1. A mineral which is very clear. 2. Glass which can be seen through.
culvert (kŭl′vērt), *n.* A drain or sewer under a road.

D

dangle (dăng′g'l), *v.* To hang loosely.
dapper (dăp′ēr), *adj.* Neatly dressed.
deputies (dĕp′ū·tēz), *n.* Persons who help the sheriff.
dismay (dĭs·mā′), *n.* Alarm and fear.
distracted (dĭs·trăk′tĕd), *adj.* Worried and confused.
dodger (dŏj′ēr), *n.* A small cake made of corn meal.
don (dŏn), *v.* To put on.
drowsy (drou′zē), *adj.* Half-asleep.
dugout (dŭg′out), *n.* A shelter dug out of a hillside.
dusk (dŭsk), *n.* Darkness.

E

earnest (ēr′nĕst), *adj.* Serious; not playful.
ember (ĕm′bēr), *n.* A piece of burning coal or wood.
emigrant (ĕm′ĭ·grȧnt), *n.* A person who moves from one country to another to live.
emphatic (ĕm·făt′ĭk), *adj.* Given special importance or force.
encouragement (ĕn·kûr′ĭj·mĕnt), *n.* What is said or done to make another person feel better.
enormous (ė·nôr′mŭs), *adj.* Very large.
error (ĕr′ēr), *n.* A mistake.
etched (ĕcht), *v.* Cut into.
event (ē·vĕnt′), *n.* A very important happening.
excellent (ĕk′sĕ·lĕnt), *adj.* Very good; fine.
expanse (ĕks·păns′), *n.* A wide open space, such as an ocean or a large area of land.

| ō, ōld | ô, fôr | oi, boil | ~~th, then~~ | ū, ūse | ŭ, ŭs |
| ȯ, ȯbey | ŏ, ŏdd | ou, out | th, thin | û, bûrn | |

expectancy (ĕks·pĕk′tán·sē), *n.* Eager waiting.

expedition (ĕks·pė·dĭsh′ŭn), *n.* A group of people making a special journey, such as a hunting expedition.

experience (ĕks·pēr′ĭ·ĕns), *n.* Learning by doing or feeling something.

extend (ĕks·tĕnd′), *v.* To stretch out.

F

feeble (fē′b'l), *adj.* Weak and tired.

flicker (flĭk′ĕr), *v.* To move unsteadily; to waver or flutter.

flourish (flûr′ĭsh), *v.* To do something in a showy way.

foreign (fôr′ĭn), *adj.* Whatever is outside of your own country or knowledge.

forlorn (fôr·lôrn′), *adj.* Alone and unhappy.

frolicked (frŏl′ĭkt), *v.* Played gaily; romped.

frontier (frŭn·tĭr′), *n.* Settled country on the edge of the wilderness.

furious (fū′rĭ·ŭs), *adj.* Very angry.

G

gale (gāl), *n.* A strong wind.

gallant (găl′ánt), *adj.* Brave and polite.

glitter (glĭt′ĕr), *v.* To shine like gold.

globe (glōb), *n.* Something shaped like a ball.

glorious (glô′rē·ŭs), *adj.* Wonderful; grand.

gnarled (närld), *adj.* Twisted.

goad (gōd), *n.* A stick used to keep animals moving.

goatee (gō·tē′), *n.* A short, pointed beard.

gouge (gouj), *v.* To dig holes in.

graduate (grăd′ū·āt), *v.* To move to a higher or more difficult place.

granite (grăn′ĭt), *n.* A hard rock.

gravity (grăv′ĭ·tē), *n.* The pull of one object on another.

grenadier (grĕn·ă·dēr′), *n.* A soldier.

groan (grōn), *v.* To cry out as if hurt or in pain.

groom (grōōm), *v.* To brush and comb an animal.

ā, āte	ä, ärm	ē, mē	ĕ, ĕnd	ī, īce	ōō, fōōd
ă, ăm	á, álive	ė, rėturn	ē, bakēr	ĭ, ĭll	ŏŏ, fŏŏt

grub (grŭb), *n.* Food.

gypsy (jĭp′sē), *n.* A wandering race of people who have dark skin and dark eyes.

H

hasten (hās′n), *v.* To hurry.

haunches (hônch′s), *n.* The hips, usually of an animal.

hearty (här′tē), *adj.* Healthy and full of life.

hesitate (hĕz′ĭ·tāt), *v.* To stop for a short time.

hobbled (hŏb′ld), *v.* Walked with a limp.

hoist (hoist), *v.* To lift up.

hoodlum (hōōd′lŭm), *n.* A person who does bad things.

horrified (hôr′ĭ·fīd), *adj.* Shocked or frightened.

hostile (hŏs′tĭl), *adj.* Not friendly.

hummock (hŭm′ŭk), *n.* A small hump or hill.

hustle (hŭs′l), *v.* To gather together.

hustled (hŭs′ld), *v.* Made to move in a hurry.

I

idling (ī′dlĭng), *v.* A motor is idling when it is running slowly.

imaginary (ĭ·măj′ĭ·nĕr·ē), *adj.* Seen only in the mind.

impatient (ĭm·pā′shĕnt), *adj.* Not able to wait quietly.

include (ĭn·klōōd′), *v.* To make a part of the rest.

indignant (ĭn·dĭg′nɑnt), *adj.* Angry.

innocent (ĭn′ô·sĕnt), *adj.* Free from wrong doing.

instructions (ĭn·strŭk′shŭns), *n.* Directions.

intruder (ĭn·trōōd′ĕr), *n.* A person who comes where he is not wanted.

J

jingle (jĭng′g′l), *n.* A short, catchy poem.

jostle (jŏs′l), *v.* To push and shove.

ō, ōld	ô, fôr	oi, boil	~~th, then~~	ū, ūse	ŭ, ŭs
ô, ôbey	ŏ, ŏdd	ou, out	th, thin	ů, bůrn	

K

keen (kēn), *adj.* Sharp.
kindled (kĭn'd'ld), *v.* Set on fire.
knoll (nōl), *n.* A small hill.

L

laboring (lā'bĕr·ĭng), *adj.* Working hard.
lance (lăns), *n.* A spear.
lasso (lăs'ō), *n.* A rope with a loop at the end.
launching (lônch'ĭng), *v.* Starting, as when a boat is put into the
water.
lavender (lăv'ĕn·dẽr), *n.* A light bluish-red color.
lea (lē), *n.* A meadow or pasture.
license (lī'sĕns), *n.* A written permission from the law to do or own
something.
lusty (lŭs'tē), *adj.* Big and strong and full of life.

M

martial (mär'shȧl), *adj.* Military; warlike.
marvelous (mär'vĕl·ŭs), *adj.* Wonderful.
mention (mĕn'shŭn), *v.* To speak about.
mesquite (mĕs·kēt'), *n.* A desert bush with sharp spines and sweet
pods.
meteor (mē'tė·ẽr), *n.* A shooting star that falls to earth.
mob (mŏb), *n.* A large crowd.
modest (mŏd'ĕst), *adj.* Simple and shy.
morsel (môr'sĕl), *n.* A little piece of a tasty food.
mournful (môrn'fŏŏl), *adj.* Sad.
musket (mŭs'kĭt), *n.* An old-fashioned rifle.
mutter (mŭt'ẽr), *v.* To speak low and not very clearly.
myth (mĭth), *n.* A story made up to explain something which is
not truly understood.

| ā, āte | ä, ärm | ē, mē | ĕ, ĕnd | ī, īce | ōō, fōōd |
| ă, ăm | ȧ, ȧlive | ê, rêturn | ẽ, bakẽr | ĭ, ĭll | ŏŏ, fŏŏt |

N

nervous (nûr′vŭs), *adj.* Fearful and shy.

nettle (nĕt′l), *n.* A plant with thorns that sting.

nightingale (nīt′ĭn·gāl), *n.* A bird which sings very sweetly.

nimbly (nĭm′b′l·ē), *adv.* Quickly and lightly.

noose (no͞os), *n.* A loop in the end of a rope which can be made larger or smaller.

nudge (nŭj), *v.* To push or move a little.

nuisance (nū′sȧns), *n.* Something that bothers.

O

observe (ŏb·zûrv′), *v.* To see.

ordinary (ôr′dĭ·nĕr·ē), *adj.* Usual; that which is common.

outlying (out′lī·ĭng), *adj.* Away from the center.

oxygen (ŏk′sĭ·jĕn), *n.* A gas having no color, odor, or taste. People breathe oxygen.

P

particular (pēr·tĭk′ŭ·lēr), *adj.* A certain one.

peculiar (pė·kūl′yēr), *adj.* Strange; odd.

peer (pēr), *v.* To look closely at something.

perch (pùrch), *v.* To sit on the edge of something.

pillage (pĭl′ĭj), *v.* To rob and tear apart.

pioneer (pī·ó·nēr′), *n.* A person who is among the first to settle a country.

policy (pŏl′ĭ·sē), *n.* The course or method followed.

potion (pō′shŭn), *n.* A magic drink.

practically (prăk′tĭ·kȧl·ē), *adv.* Almost.

prefer (prė·fùr′), *v.* To like one thing better than another.

pressure (prĕsh′ēr), *n.* Force or push.

prop (prŏp), *v.* To hold up or support a thing to keep it from falling down.

pursuit (pēr·sūt′), *n.* Chase.

ō, ōld	ô, fôr	oi, boil	~~th, t~~hen	ū, ūse	ŭ, ŭs
ȯ, ȯbey	ŏ, ŏdd	ou, out	th, thin	ù, bùrn	

Q

quiver (kwĭv′ẽr), *v.* To shake or tremble.
quota (kwō′tá), *n.* The amount to be made.

R

racket (răk′ĕt), *n.* Noise; confusion.
rage (rāj), *n.* A state of great anger.
recently (rē′sĕnt·lē), *adv.* A short time ago.
reckon (rĕk′ŭn), *v.* To guess or suppose.
rehearse (rê·hûrs′), *v.* To practice.
remarks (rê·märks′), *n.* That which is said.
remedies (rĕm′ê·dēz), *n.* Cures; things that help to heal.
request (rê·kwĕst′), *v.* To ask for something.
resemblance (rê·zĕm′bláns), *n.* Looking like someone or something else.
reservation (rĕz·ẽr·vā′shŭn), *n.* Land which the government gave to the Indians.
responsible (rê·spŏn′sĭ·b'l), *adj.* 1. Able to be trusted. 2. Having the care of another.
resume (rê·zūm′), *v.* To begin again after stopping.
retort (rê·tôrt′), *v.* To answer what someone else has said.
retrace (rē·trās′), *v.* To go back over a path already made.
rim (rĭm), *n.* The edge.
roam (rōm), *v.* To wander about with no purpose.
roguish (rō′gĭsh), *adj.* Like a rogue, a fellow full of trickery.
routine (rōō·tēn′), *n.* The order in which something is done.
ruddy (rŭd′ē), *adj.* Red.
ruined (rōō′ĭnd), *adj.* Spoiled.

S

satellite (săt′ê·līt), *n.* A small planet revolving around a bigger planet.
scabbard (skăb′ẽrd), *n.* A case for a sword or dagger.

ā, āte	ä, ärm	ē, mē	ĕ, ĕnd	ī, īce	ōō, fōōd
ă, ăm	á, álive	ĉ, rêturn	ē, bakēr	ĭ, ĭll	ŏŏ, fŏŏt

scanning (skăn′ĭng), *v.* Looking over carefully.

seasoned (sē′z′nd), *adj.* Well experienced.

seldom (sĕl′dŭm), *adv.* Not very often.

semi (sĕm′ĭ), *prefix.* Half.

severe (sė·vēr′), *adj.* Hard or strict.

shallop (shăl′ŭp), *n.* A small boat.

shingles (shĭng′g′lz), *n.* The outside boards of a house.

shrill (shrĭl), *adj.* Sharp sounding.

shuffle (shŭf′l), *v.* To drag the feet.

sinew (sĭn′ū), *n.* In an animal, a tough, stringy cord that ties a muscle to a bone.

skiff (skĭf), *n.* A small boat.

sledge (slĕj), *n.* A sled.

sleek (slēk), *adj.* Smooth and neat.

slight (slīt), *adj.* Very little.

snug (snŭg), *adj.* Warm and cozy.

soar (sōr), *v.* To fly or glide through the air.

solemnly (sŏl′ĕm·lē), *adv.* Seriously; without humor.

soothing (sōōth′ĭng), *adj.* Making someone feel better.

sound (sound), *v.* To dive down.

specialty (spĕsh′ăl·tē), *n.* A certain thing which someone knows or does well.

squadron (skwŏd′rŭn), *n.* A group of people performing in a military way.

starboard (stär′bōrd), *n.* The right side as one on board faces the front of a ship.

steep (stēp), *v.* To soak in liquid.

stoop (stōōp), *v.* To bend over.

straggle (străg′l), *v.* To come a few at a time.

Strauss waltz (strous wôltz), *n.* Graceful dance music composed by Johann Strauss, a famous Viennese composer.

stub (stŭb), *n.* A short piece that is left after the rest has been used up.

subject (sŭb′jĕkt), *n.* A person under the rule of a king or queen.

sulked (sŭlkt), *v.* Pouted; acted angry.

superstitious (sū·pēr·stĭsh′ŭs), *adj.* Having beliefs that are not based on truths.

| ō, ōld | ò, fòr | oi, boil | t̶h̶,̶ ̶t̶h̶en | ū, ūse | ŭ, ŭs |
| ŏ, ŏbey | ō, ŏdd | ou, out | th, thin | ù, bùrn | |

swarm (swôrm), *v.* To gather in a large group.

swerve (swûrv), *v.* To turn aside quickly.

symbol (sĭm′b′l), *n.* A sign which is made to stand for something else.

sympathetic (sĭm·pȧ·thĕt′ĭk), *adj.* Able to feel sad because another is sick or in trouble.

systematically (sĭs·tĕm·ăt′ĭk·lē), *adv.* In an orderly way.

T

talent (tăl′ĕnt), *n.* Whatever a person can do well; a skill.

tarpaulin (tär·pô′lĭn), *n.* A heavy, waterproof cloth.

temporary (tĕm′pô·rĕr·ē), *adj.* Lasting only for a short time.

territory (tĕr′ĭ·tô·rē), *n.* An area given to some person or group to take care of.

threshold (thrĕsh′ōld), *n.* A doorway.

thronged (thrŏngd), *v.* Came in large numbers.

timid (tĭm′ĭd), *adj.* Afraid and shy.

titter (tĭt′r), *v.* To laugh.

topple (tŏp′l), *v.* To tip over.

tousled (tou′z′ld), *adj.* Mussed up.

trampled (trăm′p′ld), *v.* Walked on very heavily.

transform (trăns·fôrm′), *v.* To change.

tremendous (trė·mĕn′dŭs), *adj.* Very large; great.

trifle (trī′f′l), *n.* Anything that is small and unimportant.

trinket (trĭng′kĕt), *n.* A small piece of jewelry or fancy article.

trudge (trŭj), *v.* To walk as if very tired.

trundle (trŭn′d′l), *v.* To roll or push along.

U

ukulele (ū·kŭ·lā′lē), *n.* A musical instrument with strings, something like a banjo, played with the fingers.

ulster (ŭl′stēr), *n.* A kind of coat.

unreasonable (ŭn·rē′z′n·ȧ·b′l), *adj.* Not showing good sense.

upset (ŭp·sĕt′), *adj.* Worried and nervous.

ā, āte	ä, ärm	ē, mē	ĕ, ĕnd	ī, īce	o͞o, fo͞od
ă, ăm	ȧ, ȧlive	ê, rêturn	ē, bakēr	ĭ, ĭll	o͝o, fo͝ot

V

vague (vāg), *adj.* Not very clear.

vain (vān), *adj.* Proud because one feels more important or better than someone else.

vamos (bä′mōs), *v.* A Spanish word which means "Let's go" or "Go."

vast (văst), *adj.* Very large.

velvet (vĕl′vĕt), *n.* A soft, thick cloth.

ventilation (vĕn·tĭ·lā′shŭn), *n.* The movement of fresh air in a room.

vexed (vĕkst), *adj.* Angry.

vie (vī), *v.* To try to win a contest.

vigorous (vĭg′ĕr·ŭs), *adj.* Strong and healthy.

virtuous (vûr′tū·ŭs), *adj.* Showing goodness.

W

wampum (wŏm′pŭm), *n.* Beads made of shells and used for money by the Indians.

wary (wăr′ē), *adj.* Unsure; a little fearful.

watch (wŏch), *n.* A guard; in early days the watch called out the time every hour.

wharf (hwôrf), *n.* A place where boats are loaded and unloaded.

wheedle (hwē′d'l), *v.* To get something by coaxing or teasing.

whimper (hwĭm′pēr), *v.* To make a low, broken cry.

wicket (wĭk′ĕt), *n.* A gate or door.

wrought (rôt), *v.* Made or done.

Y

yoke (yōk), *n.* A wooden piece which fits around the necks of a pair of oxen and holds them together.

ō, ōld	ò, fôr	oi, boil	~~th, then~~	ū, ūse	ŭ, ŭs
ô, ôbey	ŏ, ŏdd	ou, out	th, thin	ù, bùrn	

THE STORY CHARACTERS

Abigail (ăb′ĭ·gāl)
Adeline (ăd′a̶ līn)
Alfonso (äl·fän′sō)
Amalai (a̶·mäl′lī)
Angeletti (än·jĕl·ĕ′tē)
Annette (a̶·nĕt′)
Aspinet (ăs′pĭ·nĕt)
Augustus (a̶·gŭs′tŭs)
Bacchus (băk′ŭs)
Barkington (bärk′ĭng·tŏn)
Benjamin Watkins
  (bĕn′ja̶·mĭn wät′kĭnz)
Bernice (bĕr·nēs′)
Bettine (bĕ·tēn′)
Carmen (kär′mĕn)
Celine (sĕ·lēn′)
Cornelius (kôr·nēl′yŭs)
Dat-say (dät′sā′)
Don Fernando
  (dän fĕr·nän′dō)
Eema (ē·ē′mä)
Folger (fōl′jĕr)
Francoise (frän′swä)
Gino (jē′nō)
Helene (hĕ·lēn′)
Henriette (hĕn·rē·ĕt′)
Japheth (jā′fĕth)
Jazbo (jăz′bō)
Johann (yō′hän)
Jose (hō·sā′)

Juan (hwän)
Kernek (kēr′nĕk)
Kingmik (kĭng′mĭk)
Lenore (lĕ·nōr′)
Mama Mia (mä′mä mē′a̶)
Marie-Louise (ma̶·rē′-lōō·ēz′)
Massasoit (mă′sa̶·soit′)
Maysel (mā′sĕl)
Midas (mī′da̶s)
Milligan (mĭl′ĭ·ga̶n)
Miranda Saunders
  (mĭ·răn′da̶ sôn′dērs)
Nah-wee (nä′wē′)
Nanah-booz-hoo
  (nä·nä-bōōz′hōō)
Nicole (nĭ·kōl′)
Noah (nō′a̶)
Nuka (nōō′ka̶)
Palea (pa̶·lē′a̶)
Pancho (pa̶n′chō)
Paulette (pô·lĕt′)
Rumpelstiltskin
  (rŭmp′l·stĭlt′skĭn)
Silenus (sĭ·lā′nŭs)
Squanto (skwa̶n′tō)
Standish (stăn′dĭsh)
Tekegak (tĕ·kē′găk)
Trojan (trō′ja̶n)
Yvonne (ē·vŏn′)
Zebedee (zĕ′bĕ·dē)

ā, āte	ä, ärm	ē, mē	ĕ, ĕnd	ī, īce	ōō, fōōd
ă, ăm	a̶, a̶live	ê, rêturn	ē, bakēr	ĭ, ĭll	ŏŏ, fŏŏt
ŏ, ōld	ô, fôr	oi, boil	t̶h̶,̶ ̶t̶h̶en	ū, ūse	ŭ, ŭs
ȯ, ȯbey	ŏ, ŏdd	ou, out	th, thin	û, bûrn	